Roles

Other Books from Nicholeen Peck

Parenting: A House United
(Enseñanza de los Hijos: Un Hogar Unido)

Popular Parenting Methods

Londyn Larae Says Okay

Porter Earns a Quarter

Big Win for Quin

Paije Takes the Stage

Family Meetings Journal

Couple's Meeting Journal

Mentoring Journal

SODAS Journal

Roles

The Secret to
Family, Business, and Social Success

Nicholeen Peck

Silver Torch Publishing

Published by Silver Torch Press
www.SilverTorchPress.com
jill@SilverTorchPress.com

A Teaching Self-Government Resource
www.teachingselfgovernment.com
support@teachingselfgovernment.com

Cover by Becky Fawson

Edited by AuthenticityPR

Library of Congress Control Number: 2016947095

ISBN: 978-1-942707-33-2 (hardcover)
ISBN: 978-1-942707-34-9 (paperback)
ISBN: 978-1-942707-35-6 (eBook)

Printed in the United States of America

This book wouldn't have happened without David and Melissa Eggertsen, Jeff Pizzino, Monica Pond and Heather Poll.

Special thanks goes to Becky Fawson for yet another brilliant cover design.

So many families have unknowingly contributed to this book by sharing their family stories with me. I have been in homes and spoken with countless families at conferences, as well as on support group and mentor calls, about the struggles they face in these difficult times to raise a family.

Thousands have shared marital and parenting problems with me. I've learned that they're not understanding their roles. Not clearly understanding one's roles leads to contention, entitlement and dissatisfaction in relationships. Thank you for taking the time to share your struggles with me, working diligently on the problems, adjusting the roles, and then reporting back with success. Without the case studies, this book wouldn't have been possible.

Finally, I don't feel I can take credit for this book. I only feel blessed to have been part of the process of making it. I am grateful to God most of all for nearly everything associated with the idea, the story, and any changes of heart that might occur during the reading of this work.

This book is dedicated to the memory of George and Bernice Gundry, my grandparents, who were living examples to me of finding happiness and fulfillment by living unselfishly and magnifying their roles. In fact, I don't know if I would have found or understood the power of my roles in this roleless world without their humble and powerful examples. Their lives, as well as the generations of posterity still living their roles because of them, are a testimony to the truth and power roles have to point others toward real purpose and true happiness.

CONTENTS

INTRODUCTION

role (n.)
"part or character one takes," c. 1600, from French rôle "part played by a person in life," literally "roll (of paper) on which an actor's part is written," from Old French rolle (see roll (n.)). Meaning "function performed characteristically by someone" is from 1875. In the social psychology sense from 1913. Role model first attested 1957.

etymonline.com

Roles. They define our rights, obligations, responsibilities, beliefs, and even who we are. How well do we each understand our respective roles? How do we teach our children about proper roles? How would the problems children and parents face change if they better understood roles? Aren't parents — whether aggressive, passive or assertive — always defining roles anyway? Why do we see the roles in today's world wrapped around so much confusion and debate when it's impossible to escape roles?

When I sat down to write this book, those questions were my key source of inspiration. I know that God is a God of order, not confusion. Beliefs have crept into our culture about the so-called proper roles of mothers, fathers, children and individuals; and these misguided beliefs have slowly distorted the way God intends roles to be. In fact, these incorrect, false beliefs and intentions are now wreaking havoc upon society's roles — and it's tearing apart families, workplace corporate

1

cultures, and communities.

The purpose of this book is to show how the roles in families set the stage for all of the roles in society. The current and ongoing debate about gender roles in society wouldn't even be an issue if the roles within families were working properly. When roles are working properly within families, families have a vision for where they're going, an understanding of who they're supposed to be, and a passion for their divine purpose.

Ultimately, all those points are what you're about to see acted out and explained in this book. I felt the best way for me to teach you about proper roles was to do it via story.

Jerry and Janet, the parents in this story, as well as their four children and the co-workers in Jerry's office, were all suffering from an identity crisis. They didn't know who they were supposed to be and how they were supposed to act in their given roles. Why? Because there were too many confusing messages in their lives. What's more, the adults in this story were never taught proper roles in their homes growing up. How could they perform their roles, let alone teach the next generation their roles?

Confusion regarding roles disappears when family members live their respective roles correctly. When roles are lived as they are meant to be, families and work environments will not only be happier and more united, but also more productive and efficient.

When most people hear the word "roles," they immediately start to feel uncomfortable. Society has groomed us to think that roles are somehow narrow and box-like. Many people think of roles as stereotypical lists they must somehow conform to. In an effort to break out of perceived roles boxes, many family members have simply exchanged one role for another, and entered a new, much more unfamiliar box. Adopting a new role is not the same thing as "roles freedom" (i.e., freedom within roles).

If you lay all roles biases aside and genuinely observe the roles discovery in this book through realistic relationships and life problems, new insight will be gained. This new insight will enable you to find more success and happiness in your life. It will also help your relationships.

When I was a young mother, my husband told me that he would not stop me from doing everything. He said that he had observed that women nowadays want to have children, raise them, run the home, and be breadwinners. He said he would allow me to do that if that was what I wanted. He kindly said he wouldn't stand in my way. I could do whatever I wanted.

As I analyzed what I really wanted and what would make me feel the most fulfilled, I realized it was to live my roles as mother, wife and woman. I didn't want to do it all, even though I could and had been doing it all. I wanted to do what was most important. I wanted to do what I felt I was placed on the earth to do. My life has been one continual blessing since I made that decision. I am more fulfilled now than I ever was when I was trying to do it all. No one is meant to do it all.

For years my spirit has been kicked and poked and prodded to write and release this book. When I first started teaching people about self-government — and how to teach themselves and their children how to create happier families — I took for granted that people knew and understood the power of roles.

Roles are a power. They prepare us to live securely and happily. They also help us to spread happiness and to support and love each other — as well as promote relationship freedom. Too many people today are in emotional and relationship bondage. Understanding roles is a vital secret to breaking away from that bondage and finding the relationship freedom and personal power that awaits us all.

Nicholeen Peck
August 2016

~ CHAPTER 1 ~

WAKE UP!

All the world's a stage, And all the men and women merely players; They have their exits and their entrances, And one man in his time plays many parts, His acts being seven ages.

William Shakespeare, As You Like It

"Honey, will you go wake Mark up? If you don't, he'll be late for class again."

"Janet, when will Mark be old enough to wake himself up?" asked Jerry as he rolled out of bed and walked toward Mark's room. "I don't think it should be our job to wake up an 18-year-old college student each morning. If I didn't wake up in time to go to work, I would lose my job. Maybe we should just let him suffer his own consequences for once. When does he get to be a man?"

"Jerry, you know he has a lot going these days. He's busy with his classes, work, homework and friends. He hardly sleeps anymore. You remember what it was like. He needs our help and support."

Jerry stopped, turned toward his wife and sneered, "Oh, I remember alright. I remember being dog-tired in college. I also remember that my parents didn't have to wake me up. They expected me to live like a man would if I was going to do something as manly as go to college. I also remember that they didn't give me one penny for that education. I had to pay for it myself. And while we're at all the things I remember about my life, I remember coming home each day and doing work with my family. I planted and weeded gardens, mowed lawns, cleaned bathrooms and did laundry. I also ran errands for my parents who were working hard to provide for our family. I don't see Mark doing any of these things. Either he is really lazy, or I am a bad parent."

Janet was used to this kind of talk from Jerry. For the past few years he would occasionally get on these tirades about how he was sure he had failed as a father. He thought his children hadn't "turned out," and he was surely to blame. Janet saw things differently. She knew that times were different, so Mark had to be raised differently than she and Jerry were raised. Mark's life was more complicated and stressful. In fact, Janet was pretty sure that she and Jerry weren't treated well as children. She would never admit that her parents were mean or anything, but she just didn't have that much freedom. As a child, her parents were always telling her what she could and couldn't do. As she remembered it, she hardly had any opportunities to make any of her own choices. If she didn't do what mom and dad said, they would really crack down on her. She was always earning "character-building time" work. Or, if Mom and Dad were in a really bad mood and wanted to be really controlling, then she would lose some privileges.

Janet always became angry when she remembered these times. She knew her parents were oppressive back in those days, and she was determined to be a more enlightened parent for her children. She would make them feel appreciated, supported and free to make any choice they wanted to make —as long as they weren't going to break some law, or something serious like that.

Jerry was different though. In fact, he was always trying to make problems for Janet's parenting plans. He had a short temper and didn't compromise very well with the children. Janet had learned a long time ago that the best way to keep everyone happy was to compromise so that she and the children could get some of what they wanted. The nice thing about this approach was that she didn't have to "die on any hills" either. People always say, "Pick your battles." That's exactly what Janet did, and for the most part it worked. The family didn't really fight that much, but then they weren't really that close either.

Long ago Jerry and Janet had given up on the idea that they could have one of those old-fashioned "Walton's," "Little House on the Prairie," or "Leave It To Beaver" type families. Those families were a thing of the past. People were much more "real" nowadays. Those people all seemed happy on television, but they couldn't have been really happy. They never had any freedom. They were practically tied to each other and got punished all the time just for speaking their minds or for not wanting to comply with silly things the parents were obsessed about.

Jerry and Janet Justice did not exercise power over their children. They wanted the children to love and treat them with respect. Leading family experts of the day said that if you gave a child too many boundaries, expectations or consequences, the child would rebel and not do what you said. The experts also said that it was better to focus on being the child's "friend" instead of his parent.

So, this was what the Justice family did: They all decided to be good friends and treat each other like friends too. The only problem was they all liked being with their real friends, but didn't really enjoy being with family — even though they were supposed to be friends.

The Justice family didn't know it, but they were living a lie. They wanted their children (two boys and two girls) to learn to respect by not requiring the children to respect their parents. Janet and Jerry hoped their children would fall in love with their family by being treated like a friend. They imagined their children would be happy members of society without ever learning boundaries or cause and effect. In the name of freedom, they spent years protecting their children from having to govern themselves, which is actually a vital skill for bringing true freedom. Janet and Jerry did not see these ironies. Why? Because no other parents they knew were seeing them either. This was just the way parenting was. Sure, it was frustrating at times, but no problem lasts forever, right?

"Jerry, you're not a bad parent. You work harder than any man I know, and you always take time to do fun things with the children. And Mark isn't lazy either. He's just at a difficult phase of life. We just have to help him through it, that's all. Cheer up. There's no use getting upset before the day even begins," said Janet as she opened the curtains to let in some fresh morning light.

Jerry thought about Janet's words as he walked down the hall to Mark's room. "...You work harder than any man I know, and you always take time to do fun things with the children." He stopped in his tracks. That was it! He was working alone. He was only playing with the children. They had to learn to work, or they wouldn't turn out right. Today he was going to make a few changes around this place. He was going to teach his children to work, and he was going to teach them to accept the consequences life gave them too. No more babying. How was Mark going to work hard as a grown man one day if he never learned how to work as a youth?

Looking at the "No Parking" road sign hanging on the outside of Mark's door, Jerry made a choice. Today he would not wake up Mark. Today he would let Mark pay his own consequences. In fact, he was not going to wake Mark up again. Jerry calmly smiled and walked downstairs to put Mark's laundry in the dryer so that he would have clean jeans to wear when he finally got up.

Jerry felt happy. In fact, he had a spring in his step. He was downright cheerful. This was going to be a great day. For once he had a plan, and it had to work. It just had to. Slowly he started going over the details in his mind. After work he would stop by the hardware store to pick up some work gloves and a few more garden tools. It was autumn, and there were leaves to be raked and gardens to be winterized. When he arrived home this evening, he would gather the children and have a great family work time. He could just see it. The children would learn new skills. He would make it all fun, and they would see that doing work was okay.

Within a few minutes the family started emerging from their bedrooms. First Jasmine, age 15, walked into the kitchen with her head wrapped in a towel. She was dressed in her new wool sweater she received for the start of the school year.

"Good morning, Jaz," said Jerry. "You look nice today."

"Thanks, Dad. I'm probably going to sweat to death in this thing, but I really wanted to wear it. Dad, I need you to take me to school early today. I told Sally I would meet her to talk about last night's homework," Jasmine announced.

"Jasmine, I won't be ready by then. Maybe you better walk today."

"Walk? Are you serious?" Jasmine said as she rolled her eyes and put her hands on her hips. "Dad, it takes 15 minutes to walk there. I would have to leave before I even got my makeup done. You have to take me."

Jasmine was a high-spirited girl. She had a strong will and wouldn't take "no" for an answer. If things didn't go her way, she would hold her ground at all costs. Jerry was pretty sure his daughter didn't really know what respect meant. She was contrary too, always contradicting what anyone said just because she wanted to have a different opinion. At that moment she looked like she was going to start World War III any minute if she didn't get her way.

"What should I do?" Jerry thought as Jasmine stormed out of the room, assuming she had won the argument. "If I hold my ground she will get all mad and probably have a meltdown. Plus, Janet will probably get involved and think that I didn't 'compromise' again. But giving in will just teach her that I will always give in, won't it?"

He decided to play it cool. He would not say anything right then. Instead, he'd wait until Jasmine returned to the kitchen for breakfast and say, "You better get going; you're going to be late." Then she wouldn't have time to argue. Jerry knew it wasn't the bravest way to handle the situation, but he really didn't want a battle either.

While Jerry sat contemplating just what he was going to say to Janet, Joey, their 8-year-old son, walked into the kitchen and started talking about what level he conquered this morning on his new video game. Joey always played video games. In fact, all the kids did. When they weren't at school or with friends, they were watching TV or playing video games. For some reason this bugged Jerry. He didn't really know why; every other family in America was doing the same thing. He just couldn't escape the feeling that his children were missing out on life somehow. "Oh, well," he thought. "They'll grow out of all this distraction someday, right? Kids always grow out of stuff."

"Mom, what's for breakfast?" Joey asked.

"Poached eggs and toast," Mom replied.

"Ewe! Yuck, Mom! I hate that! I'm having cold cereal. Do we still have some Sugar Puffs left?"

Jerry watched with interest as Janet compromised with Joey about his breakfast choices.

"We don't have any Sugar Puffs left, Joey. So, what if you have some yogurt and toast instead?" she suggested.

"What kind of yogurt is there?"

"I think we have vanilla and raspberry."

"The vanilla is mine!" said Melissa, their 10-year-old picky eater.

"Oh, that's right, Joey. Melissa doesn't like raspberry, so she gets the vanilla," Mom said.

"You always give her all the good stuff," said Joey as he narrowed his eyes and stuck out his lower lip to pout. "I don't like raspberry either. It has seeds in it, and they always get stuck in my teeth. Besides, I asked first!"

Janet was doing her best to compromise with both of the picky children. She didn't think it was fair that they should have to eat something they didn't prefer eating, but she didn't really know who should get the vanilla yogurt at this point. She tried another angle.

"Melissa, I'm making poached eggs and toast. Would you like to have that instead? They would be much more filling. You wouldn't feel hungry until lunch," Mom suggested.

"Yuck, Mom! You know I hate those eggs. Maybe if you made scrambled eggs with cheese, then I would eat them."

"Okay," said Janet as she went to the fridge to look for the cheese.

Jerry knew that Janet loved poached eggs, but she rarely had them because the children always complained. It had happened again. He felt bad for his wife as he realized she gave so much to her family. She sacrificed her own pleasures so that the children could have what they wanted. This bothered Jerry. He saw Janet try so hard to keep them all happy. He saw her serve them all day long, but they didn't serve her. So many times Jerry and Janet had talked about the importance of setting an example for their children, yet her example of service was not being reciprocated at all. They were walking all over her, and she lovingly let them.

"Is this what parents are supposed to do? I mean, when a parent decides to have a child they are pretty much deciding to put life as they know it on hold, right? Was this what the parent/child relationship should look like?" Jerry wondered to himself. "When do the children suddenly snap out of it and grow up? Will they ever grow up?"

This was the thought that had plagued Jerry for a couple of years now. He didn't see his children wanting to grow up and take responsibility for themselves. Every day was the same. They wanted Mom, Dad, and every other adult to do things for them to make their lives easier, and they didn't ever stop their requests. Jerry had heard some people talk about how young people nowadays were caught in "entitlement traps." This lack of responsibility must be what they were referring to.

"We can't just turn our backs on our children's needs," reasoned Jerry. "The kids would fail, and then we would be to blame."

Still, Jerry thought that learning to work could help this problem. If he could get the kids to learn some new skills, then they might decide they liked doing hard things sometimes and take more of the responsibility upon themselves.

Just then a loud bang was heard overhead. Someone had slammed a door against a wall. Next came 13 thuds down the stairs.

"Dad!" Mark's voice echoed through the house.

Jerry knew better than to answer a person who was obviously angry. In his mind it was better to have the person take time to find you in order to give yourself more time to prepare for battle. This approach seemed to work well at work too. When his boss, Lance, would yell out of his office something like, "Who's in charge of the Wilson Foods account?" It was better to let his boss search and find him than to go to him when he was in that state of mind.

Jerry closed his sleepy, brown eyes and took a deep breath. Any minute he would be under pressure to remain calm. Besides, with his eyes closed he wouldn't see Janet glaring at him, as he was sure she was doing from across the kitchen at this point. Now she knew he hadn't awakened Mark. Jerry really hated facing Janet more than the kids. She was a fierce mama bear protecting her cubs. If something didn't go their way, she got mad. Even now he could feel her hot stare on the side of his face.

"Dad, I'm late! Class is going to start in five minutes. I'll never make it in time. Why didn't you wake me up? It's not like it's so hard to get me up."

Janet jumped in, "Mark, I'm so sorry. I thought you were already gone, or I would have awakened you. I told Dad to wake you up. I thought he did. What can I do to help you?"

"Make me some food. I'll have to eat in the car. Oh, I'll need to take your car. I won't have time to get gas now, and mine is all out," Mark demanded.

"My car doesn't have gas either. I was going to put some in today."

"Dad, I'll have to take your car then," Mark insisted.

"Oh, no you don't. I filled your car up last time. I think you do this to try to make it so that you don't have to buy gas. You're pretty lucky to have a car of your own. My parents only got me a bike when I was your age. Using their car was a privilege..."

Mark interrupted, "Spare me your sermons, Dad. I know. I know. The 'good old days.' Since you didn't wake me up, I have to use your car so that I don't miss the whole class."

Janet looked at Jerry with a glare that would make a badger run. He knew what he had to do to keep the peace. He gave in to Mark's tantrum again. "Okay," he said as he put his car keys on the table. "But I hope you learned a lesson about waking up on time. I won't be waking you up anymore."

"Whatever," Mark said curtly as he stormed back upstairs to get ready for school.

~ CHAPTER 2 ~

WORK

Individual commitment to a group effort - that is what makes a team work, a company work, a society work, a civilization work.

Vince Lombardi

That word "whatever" was stuck in Jerry's mind. As he silently finished his morning routine and breakfast, he thought, "Whatever." As he angrily drove Mark's car into the gas station and filled the tank, he thought, "Whatever." Maybe he could be happy if he could just stop looking so deeply into "whatever" happened each day. If only he could find a way to stop caring about the feeling at home, the feeling in his marriage — since they were both wanting different parenting styles — and the distance he felt between himself and his children. Why did he have to care so much? Was something wrong with him?

People always talk about how idealists are always frustrated because they can't ever achieve perfection. Was he a hopeless idealist who should just relax and let everything work itself out? Wait, what's so bad about idealism? If Thomas Edison wouldn't have been an idealist, we wouldn't have electric light bulbs. If Gandhi wouldn't have been an idealist, he wouldn't have been able to stop the wars in India. And what about Jesus Christ? Certainly His sermons and parables were about putting off the easy, the excuses, and the natural human tendencies to honor and serve something higher: an ideal. To develop good people, it has always been understood that they need to know what is right and wrong, what is true and false, and what is good and bad. Aren't right, good and true ideals? If something isn't completely true, then it's partly false, right? If it's partly false, it isn't true.

Because Jerry was raised in a very religious home, ideals were part of who he was. Ideals kept him focused on choosing to do what was right. Over the years Jerry always felt like he had been given a great gift by being taught ideals. He saw the world differently than others. He saw principles when others didn't. He was never okay with following the path of mediocrity. Being just like everyone else was not good enough. He had been taught to be what God wanted him to be. And if there was anything ideal, it was God. The whole idea that Jerry could live with God again someday seemed like an ideal goal too. And it brought him great comfort — especially on days like these — when life was appearing to be less and less ideal all the time. Were all those old movies and books that talked about the ideal family of mother and father working together to raise happy, respectful children true? Did people really used to live that way? Surely people didn't write lies for all of history until now. How did they do it? What was the secret, and why in our enlightened society don't we have good relationships like they did only 50 years ago?

In Jerry's mind, either people had been lying about the family from the beginning of time, or something really bad had happened to the family, and no one knew how to fix it. That's why everyone just started accepting the new normal and called it reality. In fact, some people went a step further and called ideals bad. Without ideals Jerry wasn't happy. So, maybe ideals were missing from his family too. How could he introduce ideals now, and where would he start?

"Janet would think I was crazy..." thought Jerry as he walked into Rickman Brothers Advertising Agency, where he had worked for the last 15 years.

Jerry loved the advertising world. Ever since he could remember he had spent spare moments thinking up jingles and catchy slogans, but he hadn't made it to a top position in the company yet. This was because his idea of good advertising didn't usually match management's idea. Jerry thought advertising should be inspiring. It should make people want to live a better life somehow. Advertising nowadays was always so selfishly motivated. It drove him crazy. He felt like he was tricking people instead of helping them. This feeling didn't match his ideals.

For the past 15 years Jerry tried everything possible to get the accounts for charitable organizations, community projects and health food. These ad accounts typically demanded honesty and inspiration.

"Hi, Cash, how was your weekend?" asked Jerry as he walked into the office space he shared with his good buddy, Cash.

Cash was about the same as Jerry, so they seemed to understand each other well. Most everyone else in their office were fresh off the college advertising assembly line. They all wanted to be the next advertising genius and would step on anyone in their way. Jerry and Cash had to watch their backs, or their jobs would be gone before they even knew what happened. Luckily, Jerry's projects weren't the big ones. Most people didn't want to touch a project for Caring Kidney Foundation when they could make a name for themselves by promoting the iSecretary, a phone that could instantly transcribe voice into emails, texts and business letters.

For most of the morning Jerry was silent at his desk. He had so much on his mind. What was Janet going to do to him because he chose to teach Mark cause and effect? How many lectures and looks would he have to endure? How was he going to help his children want to learn respect and responsibility? Would teaching them to work really help? It was the only idea he had at this point.

Instead of doing his work, Jerry made a list of what he would need to pick up at the hardware store on the way home from work so that he would be ready to work with the family. Four pairs of gloves, two new rakes, bags of manure, a new shovel, plastic garbage bags, and a treat for afterward. Now that he had some quiet time to think, Jerry put the thought of working as a family in the yard into his ideal world. He could just see everyone talking about the day and sharing smiles, laughs and deep thoughts with each other. They would have no interruptions from electronics because they would be outside. "It will be so great!" he thought.

When Jerry was a little boy, he and his family regularly worked together. In fact, most of his memories of his family were work memories. It wasn't that they didn't do fun things like go to movies and to theme parks. It was just that those playtimes weren't as memorable as the work times. Jerry remembered helping his father put a new roof on their family home. It wasn't an easy project. The roof was a flat roof with all kinds of problems. His parents had long wanted to have a nice pitched roof. This meant installing new trusses and learning major building skills. Jerry's dad was a school teacher, so he didn't have money to pay contractors. He learned how to do everything he could himself — even if it took months longer, which it always did.

One night, when the old roof was completely scraped off and the new trusses were covered with plastic to keep the water out of their house, a strong wind hit the house. The only people home were Jerry and his father. Dad said, "Jerry, I need you to come up with me on the roof now. There's a storm, and we need to cover up the roof again. Get some warm clothes on."

For what seemed like hours in the wind and pouring rain, Jerry and his father covered their house from the storm. They yelled to each other, threw the staple gun across the roof to each other, and worked really hard. By the time they got back into the lonely house they were soaking wet, extremely united and blissfully happy. They had the kind of happiness that only comes from conquering hard things with someone you love. Dad and Jerry dried off, made hot chocolate, and talked about the great experience they just had, as well as how Jerry's life was going. Jerry was 15 years old at the time.

Jerry tried to imagine having this kind of experience with Jasmine...

In his young years, Jerry also worked alongside his brothers, sisters and mother. Mother was always doing some grand project like spring cleaning the house, making bread, or canning fruit from the garden. Every Saturday morning the family went outside and worked in the yard for a few hours before they had an enjoyable day off. "Yes," thought Jerry, "Work had to be the answer to the problems at home."

"Jerry, are you okay?" asked Cash. "You look like you're off somewhere else today. Are you done with the kidney donation campaign yet? We have a meeting about it right after lunch."

"Thanks for bringing me back to earth, Cash. My brain is working overtime today. Everything is crazy at home. I feel like I drove away from World War III this morning. I think I've probably not been that productive this morning. Luckily, I don't have too many details to add to the proposal. I'll finish up during lunch," Jerry answered "How are you doing over on that side of the office today?"

"Pretty good, I guess. I don't seem to have any creative juices flowing lately. My problem is probably stuff at home too. My oldest daughter is really 'on one' lately. She's 13, but I think she believes she's 25. She doesn't seem to listen to anything I say. She does this eye roll thing every time I talk to her. It has gotten so bad that if I say, 'How was your day?' she just rolls her eyes and walks away. It's like my own daughter doesn't even feel like I'm worth wasting breath on. I must really be a bad father or something. I have no idea what I've done to make her hate me so much. I've tried really hard to make her happy. Have your kids ever treated you like that? I think I need advice."

"I wish I could give you advice, Cash. I don't have the parenting answers either. Sometimes I think it might be easier to invent the cure for cancer than it is to invent the cure for attitude problems. I have a whole house full of them. My kids pick their days with me. Sometimes they talk to me, but usually we're pretty disconnected. I guess I need advice too. Some people say kids grow out of stuff like this. Honestly, I'm not sure they do. My oldest is 18, an adult, but he still treats me disrespectfully too. I don't ever remember being that way to my parents. When did people determine that children grow out of bad behaviors? It had to be after I was grown. Anyway, I don't really think growing has anything to do with why they choose to stop their bad behaviors. I think that they finally learn cause and effect. I know that I totally blew it the first time I made an advertising proposal to a big client. The next proposal was better. Not because I grew older, but because I learned cause and effect, and I grew wiser. I am starting to wonder if failure isn't actually a good thing for people. This probably doesn't make any sense. I just can't seem to stop trying to figure out the way my family is acting too. Sorry I'm not more help."

"Well, at least I know I'm not alone. Sometimes I find myself counting how many years I have left until they leave my house, but then I immediately feel guilty. A good parent doesn't feel that way. How come I haven't figured out how to raise happy children yet?" Cash said with a sigh.

"You've counted the years too? I've done that so many times. I'm with you. That's not the best parenting attitude to have, but it's all I can do to get by some days. Besides, I thought I only had to count to 18, but Mark is 18 and doesn't act like he even wants to be an adult. I'm starting to wish I never showed him that Peter Pan movie when he was a kid. I think that 'never-grow-up' attitude really took root," Jerry sympathized.

There was a knock at the door. "Hi, guys," said Rick as he fell into the nearest chair, obviously frustrated. "The boss is up to his old tricks again."

"What is it this time, Rick?" asked Cash with partial interest.

Rick was one of those guys who always created drama around

the office. He thought everyone was out to get him somehow and just didn't seem to ever give people the benefit of the doubt. Everyone still liked talking to him because he often gave them helpful information about their superiors.

Rick continued, "Lance is so controlling. I just heard him talking to Jacky about how this year we'll need to work the day before Thanksgiving, and we won't even get any holiday pay. Last year we didn't have to work on the day before Thanksgiving."

"Well, it's not really a holiday on that day, and I guess they do give us the Friday off after Thanksgiving," said Cash.

"Yes, but they have *always* given us that day off. Who's he to change the rules on us? I say we strike and just don't show up. What are they going to do, fire the whole company?" added Jerry.

"Good idea," said Rick. "I'll go around and tell people what's happening and get support. Can I tell them that you guys are in on the strike plan with me? Since you have both been here the longest it would really rally the others."

Cash hesitated. "Uh, well. I'm not sure how I feel about that, Rick. If other people like the idea, then you can tell them I do too. Okay?"

"That goes for me too," said Jerry. "I don't want to be the only person mentioned."

"Great, guys! This is perfect!" said Rick as he darted out of the office.

"Ya know, Cash, I was kind of kidding about the strike thing, but I guess it's time we stand up to all the tyrannical things that happen around this office. No one even asks our input about stuff. It's like we're here just to do what Lance says," said Jerry.

"Lance is a better boss than some others I've had, but you're right. He is getting pretty full of himself. I think someone needs to show him he isn't as powerful as he thinks he is. Maybe we can do some good," said Cash.

~ CHAPTER 3 ~

WORKING TOGETHER

Opportunity is missed by most people because it is dressed in overalls and looks like work.

Thomas A. Edison

A t 5 p.m. Jerry walked out of the office satisfied that he had pleased the president of the Caring Kidney Foundation with his new ad campaign ideas. "At least something went right today," he thought as he buckled his seat belt.

At 5:30 p.m. Jerry walked out of the local hardware store with all the things on his list for the first family work night in the history of the Justice family. He even made sure to get cute, colored gloves so that the girls would feel excited about getting their hands dirty.

At 5:45 p.m. Jerry walked out of the best doughnut shop in town. His wife hated all the sugar in doughnuts, so they were a really big treat for the kids. These will surely be motivating for everyone. He could see it now. The whole family having juice and doughnuts on the back patio while they wiped the sweat from their brows and talked about a job well done. It was going to be beautiful.

At 6 p.m., 45 minutes later than usual, Jerry walked in the front door of his modest brick home on Oak Street.

As he walked into the kitchen, he noticed the table was set for dinner. "Where have you been, Jerry?" asked Janet. "Dinner was ready a half hour ago. It's probably cold."

"Oh, no," thought Jerry. "Janet likes things on time and hates to be kept waiting. I should have told her I would be a little late today. I guess I was just a little too excited."

Jerry began, "I'm sorry, honey! I have been planning a little surprise for the family. We're going to have a special night tonight. I guess all the preparation took more time than I thought it would."

"A surprise, huh?" responded Janet. "That isn't like you. Sounds exciting. I think everyone should be home tonight. We don't usually do too many things on Mondays."

"I think it is just what this family needs right now. It should be fun," said Jerry.

During dinner the kids tried to guess what kind of surprise Dad had planned.

"Is it a new video game?" asked Joey.

"Nope."

"Is it tickets to the new movie, 'Love's First Bite'?" asked Melissa.

Before Jerry could answer, Mark interrupted from the other room. He often ate his meals while watching ESPN. "Dad doesn't like those girly flicks. He would pick tickets to something better like 'Machine Men Save the Planet.'"

"It's not tickets," said Jerry.

"Well, if it's not movie tickets and it's not a new video game, maybe Dad got us those new cell phones we all wanted. Or maybe he got us a new laptop," said Jasmine.

"Nope," said Jerry.

"You're being so mysterious, Jerry. Maybe give us a hint," suggested Janet.

"After dinner we can all go outside, and I'll show you," said Jerry.

Janet started to blush. She had wanted a new car for Mark for some time now. She wondered if maybe Jerry felt bad about what happened that morning and was going to patch it up with a surprise new car.

Joey ran to the window to look outside. At 8 years old he didn't really believe in waiting for surprises.

While Janet cleaned up the table and dishes, Jerry went out back to get things ready for the family work night. When he was done, he texted Janet to tell her to bring all the kids into the backyard.

One by one, the family emerged.

"What's all this, Dad?" asked Joey. "Are we going to dig for gold or something?"

"No, Joey, we're not going to dig for gold. We're going to do something much more valuable than that," replied Jerry.

Jerry started handing out the brand new gloves to his children. While doing so, he recited the speech he had prepared on the way home from work. "I want to give you all a gift. This was a gift that was given to me by my parents when I was a boy, and I think you're ready to have this gift too. This gift will help you grow up happy and help you be successful adults one day..."

"Oh great!" groaned Jasmine. "It's one of those 'it'll-be-good-for-you' surprises."

"Give this a chance, Jasmine. You don't even know what it is yet," said Jerry. "Maybe you'll like it."

"If you like it, I most likely won't like it," said Jasmine.

Jerry ignored her comment because he didn't know how to make her stop and didn't want her to sabotage his grand plan. "My fondest memories of growing up are of the times when I worked with my family. We became such good friends. Tonight I'm going to give you the gift of work. We're going to have a fun family work night. We can all talk and work together to get the yard ready for winter," said Jerry.

"What?" said Mark. "This is your big surprise? I'm busy Dad. I've got schoolwork to do. Sorry that I'll have to miss it. You guys have fun."

Mark walked into the house and slammed the door. Everyone

watched him walk away and then looked at Jerry.

"Yeah, I'm way too busy too, Dad. I have this thing to do. It'll take all night," said Jasmine as she quickly followed Mark into the house.

"Well, I'm not going put my clean hands into those silly garden gloves and ruin a perfectly good manicure. Besides, it's not fair that Joey and I have to do it all," announced Melissa as she also walked away.

"Yeah, it's totally not fair!" said Joey as he ran after Melissa into the house.

Jerry was starting to get angry. His heart was pounding. His head was pounding. He felt like he had fire burning in his stomach. Any second he was going to explode. He ran to the back door of the house with Janet following.

Janet hollered, "NO, JERRY! IT'S NOT WORTH IT!"

Jerry opened the back door and yelled louder than he had probably ever done in his life. "MARK, JASMINE, MELISSA AND JOEY! GET BACK OUT HERE RIGHT NOW!!"

No answer.

"IF YOU DON'T COME, I'M GOING TO TAKE YOUR PHONES AWAY!" Jerry yelled.

No answer.

"I BOUGHT DOUGHNUTS FOR A TREAT!"

Still no response. "How can they ignore me?" he wondered. "Don't they have any respect at all?"

Jerry sat down on the back steps and hung his head. What a failure that was. His own children wouldn't even lift a shovel with their father for one night of their long lives. How could he have any impact on them at all?

Sitting down, Janet said, "What were you thinking, Jerry? Did you really think this little trick would work to make the children love work? You're crazy. Our children work hard at school all day. The last thing they need is us slave-driving them at night. They would just hate us."

"Seems to me they already do," retorted Jerry. "Do loving children run away from their parents when the parents ask them to do a little work? Yeah, you're probably right. I am crazy! I thought children were supposed to be taught by parents. That is just crazy!"

Janet knew where Jerry was going with this. "He just woke up on the wrong side of the bed today," she thought. "Listen, Jerry. I know you have had a bad day, but it's not our fault. The children don't really need to be taught as much as they need to be supported. Their lives are really hard. They don't need us making their lives harder by putting all these demands on them."

"Their lives are hard?" questioned Jerry. "We do everything for the family. They give nothing. I'd say we are the ones with hard lives. When are they going to support us?"

"They're just children. They shouldn't have to do all the work around the house. They'll have plenty of years to do that later," said Janet as she walked into the house to finish the dishes.

"What's the use?" thought Jerry as he picked up one of the new shovels and threw it across the yard. It hit the wood fence with a thud.

Jerry immediately knew he had lost control. He used to have a really bad temper but had been trying to keep it under control for years. Today it was like someone had taken his last hope for happiness away. Now what was he going to do? He didn't have any more ideas.

"Is everything okay, neighbor?" said a wrinkled, old face popping over the fence. "It sounds like someone's firing a cannon over here." It was Mr. Olton Sage, an elderly man and long-time neighbor of the Justice family. Those who knew him always called him by his last name.

"Hi, Sage. I wouldn't be surprised if someone in my family does start firing a cannon soon. It's like World War III over here. No matter what I do, I just can't seem to unify my family. We're all going in different directions," explained Jerry as he slowly walked over to the fence.

"Well, if there's one thing I know about, it's war," said Sage. "I served in the army during World War II. Maybe some of the things I know about winning a battle can help you."

"I'm up for anything at this point," said Jerry, anxious for any distraction from the chaos. "I'll be right over."

If Jerry was completely honest with himself, he would have admitted that the only reason he felt inclined to go over to Sage's house that night was to get away from his own house. He didn't want to go home until it was time to go to sleep. He needed a fresh, new start in the morning. As far as the battle was concerned, he was retreating.

~ CHAPTER 4 ~

LESSON ONE

Confidence is found by acknowledging and serving truth, and confidence is lost by experiencing confusion.

Sage

Jerry made his way over to Olton Sage's modest 1950's brick rambler. Sage had built this home right after he returned from Germany, following World War II. The yard was always neat and tidy, and the home was kept in perfect repair. Sage was a do-it-yourself kind of guy who believed in working hard and living by principle.

Sage was kind of a hero to Jerry, even though Jerry would probably never say it out loud. Sage was strong. He was a leader in his church, his community and his family. He and his wife seemed like the happiest elderly couple that ever existed. He always wore a smile on his face. To top off his perfect bio, Olton Sage was a war hero. He had received multiple medals of honor for his war service and willingness to bravely put his life on the line for others. From the time Jerry was a little boy he thought soldiers were cool. He wanted to be brave like them.

As Jerry rounded the corner of Sage's house leading into his backyard, Sage said with a smile, "Hi, Jerry! Come have a seat in my office."

"Pretty big office, Sage," said Jerry responding to Sage's playful attitude. "How often do you work out here?"

"Oh, pretty much every day. I have more work to do than one man can get done in a lifetime. I won't ever be done with all my projects, so I just whittle away at them a little bit each day. Besides, it gives Abigail some time to read her book. If I'm around, she doesn't take the time to relax. She always wants to work with me, but everyone needs a little bit of relaxation time. I relax by working. She relaxes by reading. Don't get me wrong. I love reading too. I read every night, but I love how clearly I see things when I work in the yard. When I work, my mind is free to think and problem solve all on its own. A relaxed brain is a beautiful thing."

Jerry knew exactly what Sage was talking about. Jerry also enjoyed how clearly his mind could think when his hands were busy.

"My brain isn't very relaxed right now, Sage. In fact, it kind of feels like it's going to explode. My family feels so selfish all the time, and Janet and I can't agree on the best way to fix the problem. I think she probably thinks I'm insane. She doesn't even seem to think our family has a problem, but I see problems. The children are lazy. They won't take any responsibility for themselves, they're demanding, and they won't do anything I tell them to do. They act like I make life hard on them, and they continually have attitude problems. Janet seems to share their opinion. She tells me to compromise with them and support them instead of teach them. She says their lives are hard and that me asking them to work is not good parenting. I see things totally opposite. It seems to me that since forever and ever parents have known that the reason God gave them children was to teach them and prepare them to live good adult lives. How could all the generations before now have been wrong? I think our society has gone too far. In the name of progress we've stopped being parents. At least that is how I feel, but I don't know what to do about it. No matter what I try, I fail.

"Take tonight for instance," Jerry continued. "I had this great idea to have a family work night like my parents did when I was growing up. To sweeten the deal I even got a special treat to eat after we were done. As soon as I mentioned my plan, the family revolted. They ran into the house and didn't even bother saying anything to me when I called them back. Janet pretty much told me I was insensitive to suggest that the children work since their lives are already so hard. Then she went inside too. That's when I exploded and threw the shovel at the fence. Sorry, Sage.

"I wish I could say the problem was only at home. My boss is getting more and more tyrannical too. It's like I don't have a voice or a place to hang my hat. Honestly, Sage, I'm starting to wonder if my ideals are just a little too high."

"Ideals are never too high," said Sage. "If they weren't high, they wouldn't be called ideals. That's the whole point of an ideal. However, an ideal isn't something you ever really achieve. It's something you work toward each day. Maybe that's where you are getting frustrated. It sounds like you've put in a lot of work today, and in the end your expectations weren't met. That doesn't mean your attempt was pointless, though. You found a principle, work, and you know your family needs to learn it. Your family wasn't prepared for your presentation, but that doesn't mean you should give up. Before you can introduce something like family work time to a group of selfish people (I hope you don't mind me using that term for your family since you used it first), you have to strengthen the relationships."

Jerry answered, "No, I don't mind. You're right, Sage. My family is selfish. Well, maybe everyone except my wife. All she does is serve and spoil those kids."

"Jerry, your wife is selfish too. The reason she coddles and spoils them is so that she doesn't have to go to the emotional effort of correcting them and saying, 'No.' Also, if she gave them everything and expected nothing, then she can feel guiltless if they don't turn out right. She won't ever have to feel responsible for their unhappiness or failures," Sage said.

Now Jerry's mind was running to catch up with Sage's wisdom. He said, "I never thought of that before. You're right. In fact, even I am selfish because I want everyone to see things my way. Sage, you said I need to work on my relationships before I can teach a principle like work to my children, but I was using work to help strengthen our relationships. When I was a child, my relationship with my parents grew strong while we worked hard together."

"Ah, I see. Now I know why that was your first approach at solving your family disconnection problem. However, I bet you didn't factor in the fact that your parents consistently worked with you from the time you were a baby. The family work and the relationship were complementary. It was a regular part of life. Also, your parents view you differently than your children see you. Your relationship with your parents was completely different from the kind of relationship you have with your family members.

Sage then began his analogy of the wagon wheel.

"Jerry, every time I feel like correcting a child, or anyone for that matter, I always think of a certain image of a wagon wheel. An image of a wagon wheel is the perfect illustration for the balance of teaching important principles, correcting when necessary, and building a strong relationship with a child.

"A wagon wheel has a very thick piece of wood in the middle called the hub of the wheel. This piece carries the bulk of the weight of the load and must be strong. The hub of our image represents your core values, beliefs, morals and principles. Those all play a role in family work.

"Coming out from the hub are the spokes of the wheel. They represent everything a parent teaches a child, from proper hygiene and manners to math and reading. The reason the parent feels a need to teach the child those things is because of the values those things are rooted in.

"Finally, there's the rim of the wheel that holds all the spokes tightly into the hub. The rim represents core values and the relationship between the parent and the child. If the relationship is not good and strong, then the whole wheel will fall apart. The teaching will fall out of the core values, and the wheel will not perform its proper function. You see the relationship is vital for a parent to be able to teach a child."

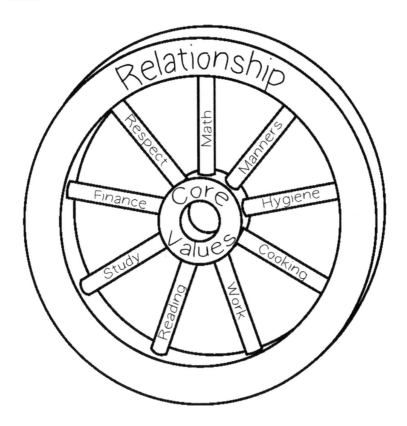

Jerry was silently taking in what Sage had suggested. Sage said that his relationship with his parents was already strong and established before the principles were taught. Sage also said that Jerry and his kids didn't have the same kind of strong relationship. In fact, Jerry was pretty sure at this point it was a relationship with a negative feeling. The part that seemed to stick out most in Jerry's mind was, "...you saw your parents differently than your children see you."

"Why, Sage?" asked Jerry in desperation. "Why would I see my parents as parents, but my children don't see me that way? That's what you mean, right?"

"It's not that your children don't see you as a parent. They know you're a parent. It's just that your children don't know what a parent is."

"What? I don't think I follow you."

"Let me explain," began Sage. "When I was a little boy, about 80 years ago now, I used to cause trouble from time to time. I liked to make people laugh and get attention. I sometimes even liked negative attention. Well, I was rather fond of paper airplanes. I could fold a really great paper airplane. They were good gliders and would get people really distracted.

"One day in a children's church class I threw a paper airplane, and it got stuck in the teacher's hair. This behavior was not acceptable, so she took me to see the church leader who we called a bishop. He was the man who was in charge of keeping church orderly. This wasn't the only time I got sent to the bishop's office, or the principal's office for that matter. The bishop had a long talk with me about who my teacher was. Not her name or anything silly like that. He spent time talking about her role in my life, and her responsibility to her students. He then informed me that because of his position as my bishop, he needed to contact my parents and talk to them about the situation because they were really in charge of me. This little story may seem out of place, but I assure you it's key to what your children, and possibly our society, are missing.

"This situation is an example of how people, not too long ago, really understood roles in society, communities and families. My teacher understood her role as a teacher. She knew that she had a duty to govern her class with principle and to teach all the students. She knew that if one student was destroying her class environment, her responsibility to the other students was more important than dealing with the behaviors of the one student. She also knew that the bishop's role was to watch out for all the church members and keep the spirit of reverence in the building. When a church member had a problem, and at this time I had a problem, then the bishop needed to help out. The bishop also knew the teacher's role and his role. Likewise, he knew and respected the role of my parents. And I promise you, my parents corrected me for that misguided missile — as well as other necessary times during my upbringing.

"The other really important part of this story is the fact that all the adults also knew my role as a child and student. My role was to learn and obey them. Their roles were to teach, lead and correct me. We all knew these roles and accepted them. These roles had to be respected, or else I couldn't have become the kind of strong, self-governing adult I was meant to be. Even though I rebelled from time to time, I still knew what making the right choice looked and felt like.

"I'm wondering if you and your wife have forgotten what the child role is at times. In today's world, parenting looks like chasing a butterfly. Parents try to sneak up on their children and trick them into the trap called obedience. The child resists, so the parent runs faster and tries to become sneakier until the child is caught and forcefully made to obey. It's like they're in the net. And as soon as they see their child get accustomed to the new surroundings of the net, they feel bad for the little captive and set it free again. The whole process is flawed.

"Today good parenting is made to appear very extrinsic and tricky. For instance, becoming a Facebook friend with your child is supposed to make a parent feel like they're teaching their child proper social boundaries. And giving a young child a cell phone is supposed to teach them to check in with Mom and Dad more. What if parents deliberately taught proper social boundaries and had an open relationship with their child? That would make the reason you're a Facebook friend legitimate. You would be a contact he or she would want to have.

Don't get me wrong. It's good advice, at the very least, to monitor your child's friends and comments on Facebook — especially if the relationship is ruined. But there's an even better approach. What if the child was taught to follow instructions and report back to parents from a young age? What if the child was taught to have that much respect? This is how it was in my time. Then the parent could put off handing their child that phone. A personal cell phone is really an adult tool, and it's led to the moral destruction of so many naïve individuals," concluded Sage.

Jerry didn't know whether to think worse of himself, to be offended at the attack on his culture, or to be in awe of Sage's wisdom. He said, "Sage, I've never heard anything like this. And honestly — I feel a little bad. I've done both of those things. Even my 8 year old has a phone. I have to tell you, I really felt like a good dad when I gave them all that stuff like the cell phones, the video games, the computers... I thought I was preparing my children for the information age and the new way to communicate. Plus, people always talk about how phones keep kids safe nowadays. Are you trying to tell me that I have maybe destroyed *real* communication in the process and maybe even put my kids at risk? It also sounds like you're saying that I thought my role as a father was to give them stuff and fight to make sure the stuff doesn't hurt them. What a ridiculous image to have of myself.

"I am also hearing you say that not too long ago children still made mistakes, but adults knew they had a responsibility to fix the problems. Is that right? So, I'm not losing my mind, am I?" wondered Jerry.

Sage rubbed his chin with his thumb and index finger while he tried to figure out a gentle way to break the truth to Jerry. "No, Jerry. It sounds like you were raised by really great parents who, for the most part, understood their roles. I'm guessing that somewhere along the way they kind of turned you loose or lost your respect, because you haven't felt confident in what you know about parenting. Confidence is found by acknowledging and serving truth, and confidence is lost by experiencing confusion."

Jerry got really excited. "You got it, Sage. As far as I can remember, my parents didn't really ever turn me loose. I went to school and church, spent time with friends, and did chores at home like everyone else. I think I lost respect for them. I'm not really sure how it happened. One day they were the coolest people in the adult world, and the next thing I knew they were the enemy and my friends were my source for direction and advice. In fact, I stopped doing good stuff like going to church during those teen years when my parents were a burden. I really thought I was so enlightened then. I saw the world completely different than they did, and I promised I wouldn't make the same parenting mistakes with my children that my parents made with me. The funny thing is now my children are so selfish, and I'm starting to try to be like my parents.... I guess I am finally waking up, huh?"

The corners of Sage's mouth turned up just slightly as he said, "Jerry, your parents probably put a little too much trust in society to raise you well. That was what turning you loose looked like. And you fell into a mediocrity trap. Society and pop culture taught you that parents were dumb and friends were cool. You soon believed that security came from social inclusion instead of from family connection. You weren't the only child who fell out of love with their parents in your generation. Hey, we all thought that children turning on their parents was normal. Some people even declared it an official stage. If you think about it, it was kind of a social trap. How did any of us know? My own children experienced the same things. It was really hard on Abi and me. We thought we lost a few of them for a while."

Jerry was really listening now. This was exactly what he needed to know. How did Olton and Abigail Sage save their children from falling off the social cliff? Their kids all seemed to turn into responsible, happy adults and great parents.

"So, what did you do?" Jerry asked.

"We went back to principle," began Sage. "One of the first principles humanity was taught was identity. The first roles in the history of the world were clearly established. There were husbands, wives, fathers and mothers. That was where humanity began, so that is where Abi and I decided to begin too. We recognized that we had either lost or never really understood our identity as parents. This is so common today. I'm sure you've seen what it looks like in all of its degrees. So many parents don't dare correct children, especially those who aren't their own. So many parents don't believe they're good at parenting, so they drop the practice. Kind of like when a person decides not to play golf if he isn't good at it. When actually, he could improve with effort. These parents decide to leave child fixing to the professionals, or those people who seem to like it — like therapists and school counselors.

"Abi and I knew that God held us accountable for how we parented our children. We knew we had to keep practicing our parenting skills and finding important principles to change the hearts in our family. So we examined our roles and our children's roles very deeply.

"My favorite book is Webster's 1828 dictionary. I looked up the word 'role' in it. Did you know that the word 'role' didn't exist in 1828? I was shocked. How could God so clearly define roles at the beginning of time, but the word didn't even exist until recent years? After doing some research on the word I learned that its origin was in the word 'roll.' 'Roll' meant multiple things. A few of the meanings still stick out in my 80-year-old mind: continuous, circular, or to revolve around and around. It kind of related to the word 'role,' spelled with an 'e,' because the meaning sounded like the circle of life. One role, such as the child role, turns into another role like the youth role, which then turns into the young adult role, which gives way to the adult role. In reality, the roles keep progressing forever.

"So I wondered, 'When did "roll" become "role"?' In the early days, directors of plays were burdened with the task of writing out everyone's part and handing it to them. The drama company would have a day called 'roll day.' This was the day that each actor received a roll of paper with his part written on it. I could just imagine them handing out the rolls of paper saying, 'Here is your roll.' Well, long story short, the word 'roll' started to stand for the part you were to play in the show. Sometime in the 1800s the word 'role' was born. It meant, 'the part someone was meant to play on stage and in life.'

"Jerry, when we pondered the significance of the word's birth, we were inspired. We understood more than we ever had before about who we were and how relationships were supposed to work. Roles are not necessarily chosen. In a play, someone hands them out. Well, in life someone hands them out too. God takes care of that for all of us right from the very beginning of our lives. Our first roles are baby boy or baby girl. We don't choose those roles. Those roles come with us. As soon as we have a child, we're given another role that had to exist in order to become a parent. The roles are mother or father.

"I know this sounds really basic, Jerry. I hope I'm not boring you, but it still gets me excited to this day. The whole process is self-evident. A child can't get here without a mother and a father. When our child was made, I was made into something else. I became a father, whether I liked it or not. This title comes with responsibilities. I knew that and felt it. But when my children were pulling away from us a bit, I didn't exactly know how my role was supposed to behave.

"Jerry, the new way of thinking nowadays eliminates roles. Don't get me wrong — you're still a father and so am I, but nowadays people don't want to draw lines that put people into boxes. This basically leaves everyone without a full identity. Roles are important. They give us identity and security. Some people spend their whole lives trying to learn who they are, only to be met with philosophies that tell them it doesn't matter who they are. They're led to believe they can simply become whoever they want to be. While these thoughts sound like a version of the American Dream, they aren't.

"In order to have the American Dream, you have to already

know who you are. Once a person knows who they are, they can determine what they need to do to become better, have more impact, and make the world a better place for having been here. That's the premise of the American Dream. At the time the American Dream was born, people were acknowledging their roles and resources. They built upon the truth and the responsibilities they already had in order to become and do more and more. The American Dream can't create identities; it can only allow people to fulfill the measure of their potential, which requires knowing who you already are.

"Roles are vital to happiness and confidence. When people try to take other people's roles or don't acknowledge their own roles, they're lost, confused and unhappy. They're not meeting their full potential.

"Another thing that we realized was that roles inspire a vision for the future. Why would anyone want to grow up if they didn't know who they were meant to become? You mentioned Peter Pan. I didn't really like the message he gave about not growing up either, even though it was a clever show. If the ideal is to not grow up, then what would happen to the world? What we're all working toward is... nothing? I don't believe that at all. Roles give us focus. A child wants to become a youth, and a youth wants to grow into an adult and take on the responsibilities of adulthood. At least this is how it used to be.

"If you read older stories you'll see a theme. Youth worked alongside parents and learned skills. They gradually took on more responsibilities and graduated to adulthood as confident adults," explained Sage.

"Sage, this was what I was trying to do with the kids tonight, but it was a total failure," said Jerry. "I know you said that they weren't ready. It sounds like you're saying they have to know who they are first before they can learn to work with me. Is that right?"

"I know it sounds funny, Jerry, but yes," answered Sage. "Your children don't see you with the correct role yet. They see a father as something different than you do. They're confused. That confusion must be repaired before they'll respect you. To respect means, 'to regard, to revere or to reverence.' Right now your children disregard you and what you say and think. That has to be addressed first. Do you understand?"

"Yes, I think so," responded Jerry. "Okay, here's a kind of stupid question: Why do you keep using the word 'youth?' I'm guessing it means just the same thing as a 'teenager,' right?"

"I've been around a long time, Jerry, so you'll have to excuse my archaic language sometimes," said Sage. "I have to admit I use the word 'youth' on purpose to describe young people ages 12 to 18. The reason for me is deep. I remember when I was young the word 'youth' was used when talking about my friends and me. Only the really wild, naughty youth were called 'teenagers.' It was actually a derogatory word that meant they were not acting according to their role. They were not focusing on who they should be or respecting the roles of others. The word 'teenager' didn't really come into use in a broad sense until after the war.

"After a while I guess it sort of became fashionable to call young people 'teenagers.' The media made it sound cool, so all the youth wanted that title — but in my mind the word has always meant: 'a young person who doesn't want to grow and up doesn't want responsibility.' They don't have heroes like youth do. Instead, they have idols or icons they want to mimic. Teenagers don't value roles or family very much."

"Great, Sage! Is this supposed to help?" asked Jerry. "Now I know I've ruined my kids. They're all teenagers. In fact, I remember congratulating them on becoming a teenager when they turned 13. My wife and I would groan and then say, 'Well, I guess it's only a stage.' Now you're telling me I've driven them away from understanding their role. I guess I really did ruin my kids."

"No need to throw in the towel yet, Jerry," said Sage. "I was just explaining why we have always liked to use the word 'youth.' It's never too late to improve a relationship or give clarity on roles. Trust me, Abigail and I had to go through this same thing when our oldest were the same age because society was becoming more selfish. We also didn't think it would really impact our children like it did. Parents have to always watch for what society is teaching their children. We learned that lesson the hard way.

"Loss of roles damages families, societies and nations, Jerry. People aren't as fulfilled in life so there's more selfishness and sadness. People who don't have roles like mother, father, son or daughter, stop caring about everyone except for themselves. When people don't know their roles they also end up focusing on acquiring things instead of becoming better people. What does a person need to become better for when there's nothing meaningful coming up in life? Roles give us meaning and satisfaction in our lives. Sure, they create more work too, but they give us our identities. Understanding who we are is the number one thing that leads to good self-confidence. It seems like everyone is worried about self-confidence, but no one wants to define their roles. Those two thoughts don't match up. Confusion is bound to result.

"I know I'm probably going too deep into this topic, but I feel like it's at the root of your problem at home and at work. Think of this scenario: Let's say a person doesn't want to grow up. He's 25 years old and wants to keep life like it was when he was 16. What's the consequence?"

"Now you're talking my language," said Jerry. "I know consequences are missing from our house. I don't know how to implement them, especially since my wife is always protecting against consequences. She thinks they get in the way and are mean somehow. To answer your question, the 25 year old won't ever leave home because he will want a free ride while he plays video games and texts people all day. This is totally what I'm afraid of. I sometimes feel like it would be better if I kick my 18 year old out so that he'll learn consequences the hard way."

"What do you think would happen if you kicked him out?"

asked Sage. "Do you think he would become a man and stop wasting so much time, or do you think he might look for another person to mooch off?"

"I've thought of that too. That is probably why I haven't ever followed through with my idea. Besides, my wife would probably hang it over my head for the rest of my life if anything happened to him. If my son were to be on the streets tomorrow, he would most likely go live with a friend's parents for free or would go live with his girlfriend and end up in trouble morally. If that happened, I bet he would most likely turn to the government for help. That seems to be what lots of kids do, but I've seen some of them turn out fine after some hard knocks," said Jerry.

"True, many people learn by hard knocks and then make really positive changes in their lives," responded Sage. "Not everyone will look for a free ride forever. There's a way to teach children respect, roles and responsibilities at home, and better prepare them for adult life so that they don't have to learn the hard way. This other way takes deliberate action and is often harder than the 'do-nothing-hope-for-the-best' approach, but we did it with all our youth and they all thank us for it now. If everyone understood their roles at each stage of life, then the world would be a totally different place, Jerry. Nations, businesses and families would all be wealthier, more productive and happier. This principle used to be understood, but we unfortunately lost touch with it somewhere along the way.

"This is how we changed things when we recognized the problem in our family relationships was due to not understanding roles. First, we made a list of what each child's role was during his/her current phase of life. For instance, one of our lists looked like this..." Sage found a scrap of paper and started making a list with the carpenter's pencil he had tucked behind his ear:

Child's Role

- learner
- exemplar
- communicator
- trainee
- supporter
- goal setter

Sage continued, "The focus within the child's role includes adult skills practice, life planning, moral learning, obedience and respect, development of priorities, and education.

"We could keep listing more, of course, but you get the idea. The list could also vary depending on the age of the child in consideration. These were the kinds of things we thought of when we started trying to understand what our children really needed to be doing during the phases of their lives. A parent could also make a list of what a child's role is not."

Sage then showed Jerry this list:

Children Are Not

- in charge of where money gets spent
- in charge of what gets served for dinner
- in charge of how the family spends its time
- in charge of prioritizing for the family
- in charge of setting moral standards
- in charge of character development
- in charge of social development
- in charge of the family's sleep schedule
- in charge of Mom and Dad's emotions
- in charge of media choices

"This list could also go on and on. I'm sure you can think of even better ones than I can since your generation has been confused by all kinds of boundary lines within the family," Sage said.

"Boundary lines. I like that. I desperately want boundary lines in our house. We seem to have lost all of them as the children have grown up. We used to teach our children to show respect by saying 'please' and 'thank you.' I haven't heard those words for a long time. Well, let's just say I haven't heard them sincerely. Sometimes I hear them when someone is begging for $20 for a date. I think we're just lazy or something," said Jerry.

"Laziness is something all of us battle against, Jerry, but I don't really think that's the main reason you don't have enough boundaries in your home," said Sage. "I bet you and Janet don't really know your roles either. After Abi and I looked at the role of a child, we turned the focus toward ourselves. Honestly, it was harder to define my role than it was to define Abi's role or the child's role. I just wasn't in the habit of looking at myself in that way. I was always reacting to situations at home.

"Reacting doesn't happen when you truly understand your role. It's just an emotional response, a form of manipulation. Emotional reactions are habitually produced to try to capture the power in a situation. Some people think emotions should always be followed. I used to be one of those people. But reacting based on emotions is just the body losing control. The heart, or spirit, of the person is much more important to follow than emotional impulse. The brain will follow either the body or the heart. So, the true act of self-government is choosing to lead your thoughts and actions with your heart instead of letting your actions and thoughts lead you.

"I had stopped using my heart, which is my will. I was an emotional mess. Taking a proactive look at what I was supposed to be, in my role as a father, was really eye opening and motivating. My father role looked something like this…"

Sage showed Jerry this list:

Father's Role

- provider
- mentor
- comforter
- provider of safety
- protector
- skill developer
- goal setter
- officiator (meetings, etc.)
- supporter
- visionary
- guider
- teacher
- exemplar
- leader

"When I looked over my list, I immediately knew I had lost focus of who I was meant to be. I was the guy who was supposed to lead the family. How could I lead if I was always reacting? I was the guy who was supposed to give my children a vision of who they were trying to become. I was supposed to be their goal. They were supposed to learn from me what being happy and successful meant. How could I be that example if I hated my interactions with them?

"Abigail's mother role list was similar to this…"

Sage showed Jerry this list:

Mother's Role

- nurturer
- spiritual sensor
- guider
- supporter
- organizer
- teacher
- leader
- skill development coach
- visionary
- goal setter
- communication mentor
- exemplar

"You can see how the father role and mother role have many similarities, but they're not identical. Abi and I have always believed that men and women were made different for a reason. These lists show how we're the perfect team for raising a family. We weren't perfect, but where one person was weak the other person seemed to have a strength," explained Sage.

Jerry sat in silence for a few minutes. He was inspired. When he finally spoke he said, "This is so basic, Sage. Why don't people know this? Something this basic shouldn't seem new to me, but it is. You're right. I've never really thought about my role or anyone else's role that way. I feel like I have so much more purpose in my life just by knowing who I'm supposed to be."

"Jerry, when I learned this, everything changed for me. I understood all the roles I had and would have. I understood my role as a boy, a man, a father, a husband, a future grandfather, an accountant, and a military officer.

"Speaking of the army... In the army all the men knew their

roles. If they didn't, then the whole military organization would fall apart. Not that homes should be army bases, but they do have to have order, focus and individual stewardship. The reason we fared so well in the war I fought in was because we all knew our roles. I didn't realize then that I was living up to my role, but I was. In fact, before I even signed up for the military, I had the role of a military man forming in my head. I did the same thing when we were expecting our first baby. I started thinking about and planning my father role.

"But as time went on I forgot my role. I replaced my father role with convenience and selfishness. The same thing happens to leaders of organizations, businesses, sports teams and governments. People get lazy and selfish. They fall away from their principles and their roles, and then the purpose of the group falls apart. Think about it — what if the people in our nation didn't know their role as voters? What if the government officials didn't know their roles as lawmakers and constantly over stepped their bounds? Where would our country be?" asked Sage.

Jerry laughed. "That's a funny one, Sage. I didn't know we were going to talk politics tonight."

Sage smiled and said, "I'm not trying to make a joke, Jerry. It's true. People don't know their roles anymore. Not just in the family, but in the neighborhood, the community, the country and the world. In some of these areas we've taken on ourselves more of a role than we should, and in other areas we should analyze what our role is supposed to be and live up to it.

"That's what I did in the war. I fought for what was right during a time when Hitler was trying to turn his government role into something it shouldn't have been. The whole war was really a battle to determine what role government should play in the lives of the people. I had experienced what proper roles of government felt like in my lifetime and recognized them as right. That's why I knew I had to defend that right even if it meant losing my life.

"Some people call our generation the 'greatest generation.' I don't know about that. I like the term used by Strauss and Howe in their book, 'The Fourth Turning,' to describe my generation. The book calls us the 'hero generation.' It says that we knew what 'good' felt like and had a duty to serve that goodness. That is exactly what happened.

"The reason I like the term 'hero generation' is because it's a term that can be applied to any generation of people. In fact, according to the book, Jerry, your kids are most likely part of another hero generation. If they learn to understand roles better, they will be the greatest generation yet. Knowing roles will help them understand what's right and wrong, and whom they need to learn from and follow."

Sage went on to talk about the importance of a people understanding their culture at home and in their communities. He said that creating a home culture gives a family identity and a reason to unify. He talked about how pop culture was erasing the home culture. But, if parents are wise, they can deliberately limit the family's connection to the pop culture.

Jerry had always admired Sage. But until now he had no idea this man understood the world so clearly. Jerry was starting to wish he had taken some notes or brought a recorder. He really wanted Janet to hear this. There was no way he was going to be able to tell it all to her like Sage could.

Sage continued talking about how the morals of the people are formed in the culture they're part of. "So, if you want to change someone's morals or identity, just change his culture.

"Understanding this tells us a lot about our country too, Jerry. John Adams said that 'our constitution was made only for a moral and religious people.' Adams obviously understood that morals didn't come from the Constitution. The Constitution was a reflection of the morals of the people and would change if the people didn't stay moral.

"You probably have a certain way you think your family should be, a kind of mental constitution. But your ideal mental constitution is not honored because your children don't share your same morals. It is moral to honor parents. The Bible tells us so in the commandments. So, if your children don't honor you, then they're behaving immorally. This moral division in your family has happened because your culture has been damaged. Pop culture has probably found its way into your home and replaced home culture. It all probably happened at the same time you and Janet felt that indulging the children a little wouldn't hurt. That's what happened to me when I was raising my children. Keep your family close. Deliberately make your family culture, and it will protect your family in hard times."

Sage talked about how knowing one's role leads to feeling duty (which feeling is missing in society today). Duty is selfless and responsible. Duty is loving and courageous. It's serving all that is right, good and true — because those things serve us.

Jerry was so excited he got up and started thinking out loud while he was pacing around the patio. "I'm pretty sure that when I threw that shovel at our fence, I was throwing my duty away too. I gave up right then. If you hadn't popped your head over the fence, Sage, then I would have crawled under a rock in my house and stopped trying. I had no more ideas, but I'm not feeling like that now. I don't know what to do to fix it yet, but I know I've not been seeing things clearly. I also see that my children have it harder than I realized. The world has all but painted a target on their chests. Pop culture wants their hearts, and the youth are confused. I guess Janet was right that they do have hard lives, but I don't really think she even sees how hard it is. She thinks sheltering the children from work will make it all better, but really we just need to shelter them, period. Shelter them with family culture and understanding of who they are so they are empowered when they step out into the world. I feel like I'm tasting freedom for the first time, even though my problems are still waiting for me at home."

Sage smiled as he listened to his friend's enthusiastic remarks. "As the Bible says, 'the truth shall make you free.' In other words, understanding the truth will always set you free. And the truth your family needs is to understand their roles. Understanding their roles will lead to freedom, justice, mercy and true happiness."

Jerry stopped pacing. "I believe you, Sage, but how am I going to get my family to believe you?"

~ CHAPTER 5 ~

THE PLAN

To accomplish great things, we must not only act, but also dream; not only plan, but also believe.

Anatole France

66 Your family is selfish, Jerry. Almost all people are selfish in some way or another. But right now your family members are only thinking of themselves. You have to accept that. That's just where you are. That's not the ideal, but accepting this fact is a step toward the ideal. There's no use fighting selfishness. That only leads to more selfishness and power struggle. It's essential that you approach your family from the selfish place they're in, not from the ideal. This means that you have to choose the location, tone and words you use very carefully," Sage instructed.

"Location? Wouldn't home be the best location to talk about family issues?" Jerry asked.

"First, you're *not* going to talk about family issues. That's too confrontational. No one would ever take the time or go into it with the right attitude. You're going to talk about how you can help each family member have more freedom and happiness.

"About the location," Sage continued. "Home is where all the arguments happen. Home is where you are all in the habit of being selfish. Plus, no one is watching. Since pop culture came into your home and took over your family culture, you need to go to pop culture to start showing your children what family culture looks like again. Additionally, when a person is away from the home, they tend to unify with the person they're with a bit more. This is the pop culture way. So, take everyone on a date, starting with Janet."

"This could take days! Can't I just take them all somewhere?" asked Jerry thinking of how many dates he and Janet had had in the past year. They had probably only gone out five times. Wouldn't it be weird to have five dates, five days in a row?

"I know it seems like forever, Jerry, but these dates aren't just for teaching a lesson about roles. They're for relationship building. Changing your culture is a step-by-step process," said Sage.

"Okay," said Jerry. "But what about Mark not waking himself up in the morning and the children fighting over breakfast and not wanting to lift a finger?"

"Those are symptoms of the problem, Jerry. They will go away before you know it. Just take one thing at a time. Be patient. You have to choose to not let that stuff bug you. You have to stay free, or this plan won't work. The only way to stay free is to govern yourself with your heart. The emotions, which are part of the body, must not be followed. For now, every time something happens that you don't like, give yourself this simple instruction, 'Be calm, be calm.' I *promise* you it works. Every time Abi makes cooked greens for dinner, I think of these words and take a bite. I've never died yet," Sage smiled as he said these last words.

Jerry questioned, "So, you're saying that I should only focus on relationship building and teaching about roles right now, and when bad things happen I should just be calm?"

Sage nodded and smiled.

"Okay, Sage. I don't have any other ideas. I'll try it. The hardest part is going to be keeping myself calm. I always seem to take things so personally. I guess I've spent a long time listening to my emotions. Can I talk to you again in a week? I'm going to need some time to do all these dates, but I know I'm going to need more advice after phase one is over. How many phases are in this mission, Sage?" Jerry asked.

Sage looked at Jerry and put his hand on his shoulder. "There will be three phases of the Justice Family Unification Mission. However, I think it might be more appropriate to call the phases 'lessons.' Once each lesson, you'll need to keep talking about it and working on it. This is a lifelong change, Jerry. Not a quick fix. Quick fixes are lies. Anything worth doing is going to take some work. I know that's probably an old-fashioned philosophy, but it has served me well for many years now."

Jerry looked at his phone and noticed it was almost 10 p.m. "Janet will probably call the police soon if I don't come home. I better get going. Thanks for everything, Sage. I think you might have saved my life, I mean my role, tonight."

"Anytime neighbor! Let me know how it goes," said Sage as he walked into the back door of his house.

~ CHAPTER 6 ~

DATE NIGHT

Things can change. I can change.

Jerry

"It's only 5:30 a.m.," Jerry thought as he looked at the alarm clock for the tenth time that night. "I should be exhausted. What's wrong with me? I feel too excited to sleep. I think all that Olton Sage wisdom has taken over my whole body. Oh well, I'm not tired anymore. I might as well get up."

As he was getting out of bed, Jerry had a great idea. While looking at Janet sound asleep on the bed, he remembered that today he was going to take her out on a date. "Maybe I should ask her in a cute way like I did when we were young," he thought.

Jerry's heart was light as he made his way to the kitchen to make Janet poached eggs and toast.

By 6 a.m., Jerry walked into the master bedroom carrying a metal cookie sheet with Janet's breakfast. It featured poached eggs, a glass of orange juice, a card and a flower he picked from the pot on the back porch. Everything was beautifully arranged.

"Rise and shine, sweetie!" he said as he opened the blinds and gave Janet a kiss on the forehead. "It's a beautiful day. In fact, I'd say it's a perfect day for poached eggs," said Jerry as he placed the cookie sheet on her lap.

"What a feast, Jerry! When I saw the bottom of the cookie sheet, I thought you made me cookies," Janet said with a smile. "What's the occasion?"

"The cookie sheet is because I don't know where the serving trays are, and the occasion is in the card. Read it," Jerry said.

"Well, I know it's not my birthday, and our anniversary was last month, so I'm clueless," said Janet as she opened the card.

The card was simple. It was a piece of typing paper folded in fours. Jerry had written his sweet note with the Sharpie Janet used to label leftovers. It said:

Janet,

I love you so much! Will you go on a date
with me tonight? It's been way too long!

Love,
Jerry

Janet looked at Jerry with tears welling up in her eyes. "Jerry, you never cease to amaze me! I would love to have a date. I'm supposed to have my book group tonight, but since you made such a special invitation, I'll go out with you instead. Thanks honey."

"Thank *you!*" said Jerry as he bent down and gave her a kiss. He felt like a new man. Next he would go wake up the kids. First stop was Mark's room.

From down the hall Jerry could hear something. It was music; really up-beat music at that. Mark was already up, getting dressed while listening to his morning tunes.

Jerry's feet came to a stop before he got to Mark's door. He smiled and gently shook his head as he thought to himself, "So, Mark really can get up. I know there was probably a way better way to teach him to wake up, but he did learn something yesterday. Maybe he learned that he shouldn't trust someone else with managing his life. Hmmm… Is it bad that he wouldn't trust me though? I want a good relationship; the kind built on trust. But being late yesterday must have scared him a bit."

Jerry smiled again as he continued thinking this through. "However, is fear a good enough reason to change behaviors? Shouldn't a person want to be responsible because it's the right thing to do and because they want success? Yes, that would be the ideal. That will be what I teach him at some point — after we work on our relationship. But at least now he's made a right choice, even if it's to avoid the negative effect of a wrong choice. Maybe that's a first step for a selfish person. Sage did say that selfish people have to change for selfish reasons before they will change for principle."

His right foot started to take another step toward Mark's door, and stopped mid-air. "Wait!" Jerry thought as he lowered his foot again. "Should I say anything about his waking up? I'm really proud of him. I want to praise him, but if I praise him he might feel like I am bragging about my victory over yesterday's battle. Plus, I might be too tempted to use the praise to rub in this teaching moment. Yeah, that's my tendency. I better not talk about him waking up in time. But if I just walk by without saying anything, Mark will think that I'm still frustrated with our relationship. I've got to start unifying our relationship. Let's see. What do I do? I know. I'll just talk to him with love and kindness and not mention him waking up on time. I'll let him have his own victory. After he wakes up a few days in a row, I'll give him a good, sincere compliment about how impressed I am with his maturity."

"Good morning, Mark!" Jerry said as he took a step inside Mark's room.

"Morning," Mark said emotionlessly not looking at his father.

"I heard Dallas won their game last night. They are doing pretty well so far this season," Jerry continued.

Mark, who was sitting on the edge of his bed putting his socks on, looked up at his father. "Yeah, I watched the end of the game. I didn't see you around at all last night. Where were you?" asked Mark.

Jerry kept eye contact with his son. "I was talking to Sage. He's such a great guy. I really hadn't talked to him for a long time. We had a lot of catching up to do. I think I'm going to start visiting more often. He is a real friend."

"He's kind of old to be friends with you, Dad. Don't ya think?" Mark asked as one side of his mouth turned up into a shy kind of smile.

"The fact that he's so old is probably one of the reasons I really need him as a friend. He's smart, Mark! I wish you could have heard all the stuff we talked about. In fact, I would love to tell you. Isn't tomorrow the day you get done with classes early?" Jerry asked.

"Yes," Mark said hesitantly. Mark wasn't used to his dad really caring about what his schedule was. In fact, he was sort of shocked that his dad even knew anything about his life.

"Well, there is this new pizza place downtown I've been dying to try out. I understand they have a double-decker pizza. Mom would never go for that much grease. Do you want to go with me for lunch tomorrow to try it out? I could meet you downtown after your last class at one o'clock."

Free food at nice restaurants does something for busy college students. Before he had any time to think, Mark's mouth spoke for his stomach, "Sure!"

"Perfect!" said Jerry. "I'll text you the address."

"Since when did you text?" Mark said in a funny, surprised voice.

"Since today," said Jerry. "I still don't like texting people because it attaches me way too much to my phone. I would rather talk to people, but I do see how it could be useful for sending addresses. That way you won't lose the address either. Why? Would you rather I just call instead?" Jerry said with a humorous smile.

"No. Text me, Dad. It'll be good for you," Mark joked.

"Well, thanks for thinking of me, Mark," Jerry said with a genuine smile. "Today is going to be a good day," Jerry thought as he walked out of the room.

After Jerry woke everyone up, the morning went similar to the day before. The children ordered Janet around. She caved in trying to keep the peace, but there wasn't really any peace. Jerry still didn't know what to do to stop it all, but today something was different. Today Jerry was calm. He was determined to be patient. First, he had to accomplish step one. Fixing all that other stuff would maybe come in another step. For now, he had to be calm and trust that the relationships would be improved if everyone understood their roles.

Since Jerry was up so early he had time to plan out his week a bit. He decided that he would ask Melissa for a date tomorrow night, spontaneously check Jasmine out of school to have a lunch date, and take Joey to go play miniature golf and get a burger. He had a busy week, but for some reason this schedule didn't overwhelm him. He was really excited.

He never had a workday go by so quickly... and happily. Jerry couldn't remember the last time he liked being at work so much. He was so into his work today. His mind was free and creative.

"You're done with the ad designs for the new kidney donation campaign already?" Cash asked from across the room. "You're on fire today, Jerry. Yesterday you wanted to go on strike. Today you could be employee of the month."

Jerry looked up from his work. "Yeah, about that strike. I had a bad attitude yesterday. I started thinking about it. Lance is our boss. His role is to keep our department doing what it needs to do to keep the business making money. Without him we wouldn't have anyone to be accountable to. And what about my role? I'm an employee. I mean, sure, I should be treated fairly and respectfully, but other than that I'm getting paid to do what my boss says. That's my role. I'm responsible for my projects, obedience and attitude. I'm not signing anything Rick wants me to sign. My loyalty shouldn't be to Rick or to some future day where all I want to do is kick back and relax. It should be to my company. And really, that one little change isn't going to kill any of us. In fact, it's not immoral or anything. It's just a change, and I don't like change. Sorry about all that yesterday, Cash."

"Are you okay, Jerry?" Cash said with a smile on his face. "I've never heard you so calm and logical before."

"Thanks a lot," said Jerry with a chuckle. "I know. I haven't exactly always been the level-headed one around here. I'm pretty sure I've actually always been the emotional one, but things can change. I can change. I can't guarantee that I won't get emotionally charged again. Old habits are hard to change, but I'm going to work on it. I decided that I want freedom from all that emotion. So, that's my new plan. Do me a favor. If you see me getting all worked up about the next political issue in the office, just tap me on the shoulder and say 'freedom.' I would really appreciate having a reminder."

Cash's eyes widened in disbelief. "Who is this guy, and what did he do with my friend?" he thought. In his shock Cash managed to say, "Sure, Jerry. Anything for you."

During his lunchtime Jerry made reservations at the best sushi place in town. He thought sushi was okay, but Janet loved it. Tonight was for her. Next, he called Janet and told her he would pick her up at 6 p.m. for dinner. This would give him just enough time to pick up some flowers and put gas in the car before he got home.

At 6 p.m. sharp Jerry was holding a pretty bouquet of yellow and red roses while knocking on his own front door. He heard little feet running toward the door. He smiled. It was probably Joey. Joey loved to be the first one to see who was at the door.

The door flung open, and sure enough there was Joey looking up at Dad. "Dad, what's the matter with you? Why didn't you just come in? It wasn't locked," said Joey, confused.

"Is your mother home, young man?" asked Jerry. "I have a special date with her tonight. Could you go get Mom?"

Without a word Joey quickly ran off. About one second later Jerry could hear Joey yelling through the house, "Mom! Dad's here, and he won't come in — and he has lots of flowers! He says you have a date."

After a really long minute waiting on his own front porch, Jerry finally saw Janet. She looked great! How long since he'd noticed what a beautiful woman she was. Her long brown hair was brushed smooth and bounced around her shoulders as she walked toward the door. She was wearing a bright pink top and a turquoise blue scarf. The pink made her cheeks look all rosy and vibrant, and the blue scarf matched her beautiful, deep blue eyes.

"Janet, you look fabulous!" Jerry said.

"Well, you *are* fabulous Jerry! And you even brought flowers. I'm starting to think that today is all a dream. I've been thinking about our date all day long. In case I forget to tell you later, thanks!" said Janet as she took the flowers and put them in a vase of water.

Jerry could hardly wait to tell Janet all he learned about roles from Sage. But he didn't want to frighten Janet, so he stayed calm and patient. He wanted to start the conversation just right.

After the sushi was served and Janet had an opportunity to say how amazed she was that Jerry chose to go out to sushi, Jerry said, "Janet, I'm really sorry about what happened yesterday. You know, about not waking Mark up and about trying to make everyone work for fun. I knew we needed change, but I didn't exactly know how to do it. In fact, I still don't know how to fix everything in my life and for the family, but I do know a few things. Can I share them with you?"

Janet looked into Jerry's eyes. She could see deep into his heart. He was sincerely trying to do something the right way. She had to trust it. "Okay, Jerry. But about yesterday. It wasn't a total failure. Did you notice how Mark got himself up? I guess you were right. He really did need to learn the hard way."

Jerry responded, "I did notice. In fact, I was really surprised. He definitely learned cause and effect. But to be honest, I don't really like how I taught him to change his behavior. It was kind of manipulative. I'm hoping I can learn a more honest way to help the children choose right. Sage is helping me."

"Sage?" Janet sounded unsure. "Do you mean the neighbor? How can he help?"

"Well, last night after my attempt at a family work night failed, I made a royal blunder by throwing a shovel at the fence in desperation. Sage poked his head up over the fence to see what caused the loud crash. It led to me to having a good chat with Sage," said Jerry.

"Based on the time you walked in the door, I'd say your chat was more like a business meeting. Chats are usually shorter than three hours," Janet teased.

"True. I concede. It was a sort of a business meeting," said Jerry. "We talked about the business of raising children and being fathers. You know, now that you mention it, being a parent is kind of like owning a company. I have a certain role as one of the owners. I have to take responsibility for understanding my role and doing what's required, or the company will fall apart. In fact, everyone has their own unique role that they need to fill for our family business to succeed. Right now our family business is struggling. We are all having an identity crisis. And some of us are even engaging in role reversal. I'm concerned that if we don't get everyone understanding their roles soon, then our whole business will deteriorate."

"I'm not sure what to think about this, Jerry. For the longest time you've been saying you're a bad father, and that our children are lazy and need to learn things the hard way. Now you're saying that we don't know who we are? I'm not sure I follow you," Janet confessed.

"That's right, Sweetie. We don't know who we are. Sure, we know our names and if we're Mom, Dad or child, but we don't really know what it means to be Mom, Dad or child. I think that somehow we all got so selfish that we forgot what our job descriptions were. I know I did. I have not been living and acting like a man who understands what it means to be a father and a husband. I've just been acting like a man. A father is an important role.

"Let me show you what I mean. Actually, I'm going to let you do the showing so that you know what I mean. I'm sure you know better about what I should be than I even do," Jerry said as he got out a sheet of paper. "Tell me what a father is, Janet. If you had to describe what my role should look like, what would you say?"

Janet thought for a moment, wondering if this was some sort of trick. "The father role is to be the provider, protector and supporter. And in many ways, he should be the leader — especially morally and spiritually. He's to teach and correct the children, serve them, and be kind and understanding. But he should also be firm about correct principles, regularly praise his family, and help prepare the children for adulthood. He should also be loving, fun, engaging and connecting. He should always be willing to take the time to talk to the family and get to know them better."

"Wow, Janet! You just thought all that up right now? I'm impressed!" exclaimed Jerry.

"Well, that was the guy I married, Jerry. For a long time now I've kind of been hoping to see him again," said Janet.

Right after she said that she wondered if he would get mad at her. Jerry had been so emotional for such a long time. She didn't usually dare talk this freely, but she was so relaxed tonight she just let her real thoughts out. She looked at his face and wondered if the magic of the day would soon end. But a miracle happened; Jerry looked at her and smiled. That was it.

Finally, he said, "Janet, what you just said makes me happy and breaks my heart all at the same time. You're totally right. I have forgotten my role. I've become selfish. That's why I wanted to talk with you tonight. I think we've all forgotten who we're supposed to be. The whole Justice family is selfish, and I'd hate to leave you out of it. I think I'm better at being selfish than any of us, but you're a bit selfish too.

"Now, let's look at your role. I'll write it down. What is your role as a mother and wife supposed to look like?" asked Jerry.

Janet looked down at her plate. Thinking. This one was harder. "That's funny," she thought. "I would have thought I could think of my own role easier than yours. After all, I only have to describe what a mother and wife do, right?"

After some pondering, Janet finally said, "Well, I guess a mother is the person who makes dinner and cleans up after the family. I'm not really sure. This one is harder."

Jerry looked at her intently and then spoke, "Janet, you're way more than the woman who cooks dinner and cleans up after us all, although you definitely do that. Those things aren't your role. Those things are things you do because you love us and nurture us. I see your role as someone who nurtures, loves, teaches, serves, praises, and sets the example. You're also a spiritual leader who not only keeps the family organized, but who also protects us physically and spiritually by nourishing us and keeping the standards high in the home. The role of mother is to inspire her family, to correct her children's behaviors, to see their potential, to teach them boundaries and social skills, and to be compassionate and understanding. As a wife you also do all these things. But you also put your marriage relationship first by showing appreciation and unity. This is the woman I married."

Janet looked at Jerry with a tear rolling down her face. "I'm sorry, Jerry," she said as she wiped away the tears. "I've failed you. I probably only do two or three things on the whole..."

Jerry interrupted. "It doesn't matter. This list is the woman you are. It's who you were meant to be, and I love you for it. I think we have all become a little bit distracted from our roles lately. That is why I think we all need to become focused again. I'm going to talk to each of the children about roles so that we can all be unified in our focus as a family. This will help save the family business. This will help us all be free. The more I think about it, the more I realize that our children are trying to have freedom. They want us to carry all their responsibilities, and they want to be able to do whatever they want when they want with no questions asked. But this loose, irresponsible way of living doesn't bring freedom. It only leads to selfishness and emotional outbursts, which is really just bondage. When they know who they are and take ownership for that, and when they learn how to govern themselves, then they will actually be free. So, step number one is to help everyone understand his or her own roles.

"There is one last role I want to discuss with you. I'll also discuss this role with each of our children. We all have to be unified in our understanding of what the child role is. What do you think the child role should be?" Jerry inquired.

"Well, that role is pretty easy for me. I've been focusing on it for at least 18 years now. Children are learners. They make lots of mistakes but are supposed to learn along the way. Children are supposed to have fun, learn to work, and accomplish projects and things. They need to learn adult skills and social skills. They need to learn responsibility and set examples for their family members. Children are often put in leadership positions with their siblings and friends, and so I would say they can be leaders too, but obviously they shouldn't lead parents. That would create confusion, wouldn't it? You know all that stuff you always say about how the kids need to build their character? I haven't wanted to deal with the emotions that would be involved in getting them to develop their character, but I do know you're right. If they don't learn character, morals and values now, when will they?" asked Janet with a smile as she looked shyly at the tablecloth.

"Janet, I feel like a million bucks right now. I agree with everything you said the role of child is. We're totally unified on this. There was a time when I wondered if we would always see parenting differently. I see now that we see all the roles in the family the same. That is a huge deal. I haven't felt this unified with you since we both shared with each other that we had a strong impression that our first son should be named Mark."

With tears rolling down her cheeks, Janet said, "Jerry, what is happening here? I feel like we've found some great truth, and I feel excited… and *in love*. But the realist side of me also knows that it's going to take a lot more than this to fix the relationships at our house. Let's just look at Mark. He's *so* disconnected. And Jasmine is *so* negative. And the two young ones are *so* selfish and spoiled, not to mention distracted all the time by meaningless stuff. Is there any point in even hoping?"

"Hope is all we have at this point. We can either start listening to my new mentor, Sage, and his old-fashioned ideas, or we can continue on like we've been going. But right now we're going nowhere, and we're all miserable. So why in the world would we keep the status quo? We need freedom, and Sage said he would teach me about freedom. He said it will take us three steps to right our family ship. I say we give it a try. I already have plans to have individual talks with the kids this week. I told Sage I would come talk to him again next week to let him know how we did. Having someone to check in with is really helpful. I need to be held accountable. Anyway, Janet, I've never had a day like today. I have been in love with my family all day. I haven't known how to fix everything yet, but I've seen myself with my role, and you with your role. and the children with their roles, and everyone looks different. I don't feel like I'm fighting the family anymore. Now I feel like I'm living with purpose. I know my role, and I am ready to perfect it."

Janet was listening so intently that she didn't even have anything to say when Jerry stopped talking. Silently, she contemplated the discussion that just took place, while she played with her chopsticks and a few grains of rice on her plate.

"Jerry, you said you're going to talk to each of the children," said

Janet. "Would you be really upset if I was there too? Do you want this to be just something you do, or do would want to do it together?"

"Oh, silly me!" said Jerry. "Of course you should be there too, Janet; for multiple reasons. First, it's your role to nurture and teach just as much as it is mine. Second, your relationship is damaged just as much as mine is, even though I'm the bad guy most the time when you're getting walked on. Third, we need to show the children that we're unified about family issues. This needs to be a joint thing we do. The only problem is I told Mark that we're going to a double-decker pizza place tomorrow for lunch, and that you wouldn't like it."

"Well, I wouldn't like it, but hey — I've had two of my favorite meals in one day. I'm sure I can stomach a little bit of pizza tomorrow. Text me the details, and I'll meet you there," said Janet.

"Oh, here we go with the texting again. I'm going to have to start enjoying texting," said Jerry. "I guess I pay for it, so I might as well use it. Hey, let's leave your coming along as a surprise. I don't want to change things on him. We will just say that I told you that I was going to the new pizza place, and that you actually said you wanted to come. I'm sure he'll understand."

At the door of their home Jerry gave Janet a very warm hug and a kiss, just like old times, and then said, "I had a fun time tonight, honey. Can we go on more dates in the future?"

"Actually, I did have another date in mind, Jerry," said Janet. "You said you were going to get training from Sage. Do you think I could get trained with you? Then you won't have to tell me everything. Besides, after the miracle I've seen in you and me today, I want to learn from Sage firsthand."

"That's a great idea, Janet! I don't know why I didn't think of it," said Jerry. "Of course you can come. I think you'll like Sage. But I warn you, he's extremely blunt. You have to want the truth to really learn from him. I was at such a low spot the other night that I was ready for *any* solution. Had it been any other day, I don't know if I would have been as ready for him to tell me how selfish we all were. It was really providential."

"I think I can take the truth. If I struggle, just give me a squeeze or something to remind me that I wanted to hear the truth, okay?" responded Janet.

The night was magical! Jerry and Janet were unified and excited about change. They didn't know exactly how everything was going to go, but they had to try. There was no going back. *The truth about roles had set them free.*

CHAPTER 7

DAY TWO

> If you look for truth, you may find comfort in the end; if you look for comfort you will not get either comfort or truth only soft soap and wishful thinking to begin, and in the end, despair.
>
> *C. S. Lewis*

Jerry slept like a baby. Janet even had to nudge him when the alarm was resounding through the house. "I don't remember sleeping that good in ages," said Jerry. "I'm so content, Janet. Even if we never find all the answers to the family problems, I'm already a changed man. I love it! It's going to be a great day!"

"Mark is up again, Jerry," responded Janet. "He's taking responsibility. I think you were right about our family needing to learn more cause and effect. I won't lie — I am a bit nervous about lunch today."

"Don't be nervous, Janet," said Jerry. "I learned something last night. I was really nervous to talk to you because I thought we saw parenting through completely different lenses. But I decided I had to trust the truth that Sage told me. When he told me about roles, I felt it was true. He also told me to talk to you. I had to make myself trust that the truth would win out. I had to trust that if I was honest about my faults and me and shared the true principles I had learned, the truth would prevail. The same thing will happen for the conversations with the children. You'll see. They may think it's a little weird, but they will feel our commitment and our love. Our interactions with our children are based on time-tested truths, and the roles are self-evident truths. They were born to us — and there is no getting around that. With each birth came roles. Besides, we're being open and honest. We aren't manipulating. We're honestly unifying our family with these conversations. I know this will work."

By the time Janet and Jerry made it downstairs to the kitchen, Mark was already there grabbing a bite to eat. The younger children were all busy fighting about why there weren't any clean spoons, but for some reason the scene didn't look as bad to the parents today. It seemed temporary. They looked at each other, smiled, and then started sorting out the drama as usual.

At the office Jerry couldn't get Lance, the boss, out of his mind. Lance was the leader, so did that make Jerry a follower? Or, could Jerry be a leader too? There were good reasons that Jerry had a hard time unifying with Lance. Lance was much younger than Jerry and seemed to be somewhat arrogant. That bugged Jerry a lot. Jerry also thought that Lance seemed to advocate for very shallow ad campaigns. He never got the impression that Lance liked the meaningful messages that he and Cash created.

Could it be possible that Jerry was misunderstanding Lance? Could Lance be just as frustrated at work about no one caring about his role as the boss, just like Jerry was frustrated at home with his children?

After thinking for about 20 minutes at his desk, he decided that he needed to do something. He didn't know what he was going to do, but he had to connect with Lance in a deeper way. He thought about how he would like his son Mark to want to be more helpful and about how much he loved that Mark had now done his responsibility two days in a row. Maybe he could think of himself in his employee role and make a difference in his relationship with Lance.

Knocking on the glass door that was slightly ajar, Jerry asked, "How are you today, Lance?"

Lance looked up a bit surprised at the intrusion and then, as if preparing for the worst, raised one eyebrow and replied, "Good. Did you need something, Jerry, or are you just making social calls?" There was no doubt about it; Lance's defenses were up. He didn't trust that Jerry would just stop by his office unless he had some complaint or something. Besides, Lance had gotten wind of the strike idea and guessed that Jerry might have had something to do with it.

Jerry walked a couple of steps into the office. "Oh, all's good. Hey, I just wanted you to know that I'm done with the Kidney Donation Ad Campaign, and I'm now going to start working with Cash on the Thanks Campaign that Senator Thompson wants to run right before Thanksgiving. We hope to have it done by the first of next week. Is there anything you need me to do before I get started on that?" he asked.

Immediately the boss's eyes softened, then his head tilted just slightly as if he was really taking this moment in. Then Lance straightened up and said, "I thought you wanted a strike because of having to work the day before Thanksgiving."

"I'm not going to lie to you, Lance. Some of the guys were talking a few days ago, and I got kind of worked up from the conversation. I threw out the strike idea as a shock statement. I didn't expect anyone to do anything, but I've thought about that a lot since. Honestly, I have no problem with you telling us we need to work that day. You're in charge, and I totally respect that. I'm grateful for this company and the job I have, and for you and your leadership. You have a lot of stresses to deal with that most of us never even know about. I just wish I had been more helpful lately for you. I'm sorry, Lance."

"Jerry, are you for real?" Lance asked. "Are you hoping for a raise or something? Or are you just trying to butter me up? I don't know how to take all this nice talk."

"Sorry, Lance. I know it's not normal. All I can say is I see things differently now. I appreciate your role in the company and want to support you any way I can. Just let me know what I can do. This doesn't mean I'll be perfect, but I know I can improve as an employee. Thanks for the chat," said Jerry before he turned and walked away.

It was lunchtime. Jerry, Janet and Mark were all eating a delicious, but very greasy, double-decker supreme pizza while washing it down with tall glasses of lemonade. This parent date with Mark was definitely a first. Never had they both taken him out just because they wanted to do so, and never before on a weekday.

"So, what is this all about Dad?" asked Mark. "You have me really curious. You seem to have changed a bit the last few days, and I don't know what to expect from this random lunch."

"I know it's random, Mark," said Jerry. "I'm really sorry that we haven't done stuff like this more often over the years. We really should have.

"What do you want our relationship to be like? You're an adult now, and I thought it would be a good thing to get your input on what you want your relationship with your parents to be like from here on out."

"Seriously, Dad?" questioned Mark. "I haven't really thought about this. Um, I guess I want us to be close, ya know? I suppose it would be cool if we were friends, and we respected each other. Though I don't think that you should have to control all I do and treat me like a baby forever. I kind of want some freedom, ya know?"

"So, let me see if I understand," said Jerry. "You're saying you want freedom to succeed or fail on your own, and you want to feel respected. You don't want us doing everything for you forever, and you hope to have a close relationship. Does that sound right?"

"Don't forget the part about friends," added Janet.

"That sounds about right," said Mark.

"Well, we want you to have freedom too," continued Jerry. "We want you to have the joy of your own successes and feel the pain of your own failures. We want to be close to you too. Our relationships haven't been so great lately. There has been an uncomfortable distance, and we would love to fix that. We also want to respect you and feel respect from you. I don't think we've been doing really well at that lately. If we respect each other more, I think we'll all become best friends. Friendship comes after respect for each other's roles."

"That makes sense I guess," said Mark.

"Mark, before we can respect each other, we need to know what to respect — don't you think?" asked Jerry.

"What do you mean, like a list?" asked Mark.

"Yeah, I feel we have to decide what or who we're respecting before we can make a change in our behaviors. Who we are is another way to say what role we have in the family. We all have different roles when we're with different people. At work I'm an employee, to your mother I'm a husband, and to you I'm a father. What would you say my role is as a father?" Jerry asked. Janet opened her small notebook that she kept in her purse.

"Well, I guess you provide for the family and make sure we all turn out okay. You teach us stuff and tell us when we make mistakes... I guess dads are supposed to lead their families too," answered Mark.

"Your list is similar to my list, Mark," said Janet. "Last night Dad took me on a date and asked me the same questions. I couldn't believe that I hadn't really ever thought of his role before."

The conversation continued and Mark easily listed what the role of a mother is. Then Jerry asked, "What is the role of an 18-year-old son?"

That question stumped Mark at first, but his parents waited patiently in silence. Finally, he answered, "I guess I'm supposed to do what you say as long as I still live at your house. I guess I should help out more and probably be paying for all my own stuff since I'm an adult."

"Yes! And there's more," Janet led Mark a little by asking, "Mark, what do you usually do all day long?"

"Well, I go to school," said Mark. "I guess I'm a learner. I'm starting to think the learning thing isn't ever going to end."

"You're more right than you know, son," said Jerry. "Learning is a permanent part of life. I just learned a lot about roles, and I have an 18-year-old adult son. I feel like I was a little late learning that one. You're right about being a learner. That's a big part of your role right now. What are you learning?"

"School stuff, money management, patience at home. I guess I'm still learning how to be an adult too," said Mark.

"I thought you might say that," said Jerry. "It's true. You're learning so many skills right now for school and for your future adult life. You're learning how to keep house, work, manage money, prioritize your time, and communicate more effectively — as well as all the academic subjects you're involved in. So, taking all this learning into account, how can your mother and I better respect your role?"

"I guess you have to help by teaching me and being patient," responded Mark.

"Isn't it amazing?" said Janet. "Our roles are to be teachers, and your role is to be a learner. God planned that perfectly."

"Mark, we know our method of teaching you and the other children has not been very good. So, we're going to really work on it in the coming weeks. But we wanted you to know that we want to respect you and your role. We know you want freedom and respect. As we acknowledge and respect each other's roles, we'll have more freedom. There will be less drama and less frustration. Can you work with us on trying to get the roles back in order at home? If children try to have adult roles and order parents around, or if parents get too burned out and stop teaching or fixing problems, then the family will end up stuck in emotional bondage. Does that make sense? We have to set it straight now by starting with acknowledging and respecting each of our roles,"

Jerry said.

"Yeah, I get it. It makes sense. I'll try. But I do get frustrated a lot. I guess I just have to keep remembering the roles," Mark responded.

~ CHAPTER 8 ~

DATE WEEK

It's never too late to fix the roles in your relationships.

Abigail

Day after day Jerry and Janet went on dates with the children. They took Melissa to her favorite malt shop for dinner and a shake. The discussion went really well. She could see that by honoring the roles in the family she would end up getting more of what she wanted — which was freedom and kindness. Melissa was tired of all the arguing and wanted to feel more loved at home instead of picked on.

Joey's date went better than all the other dates. Mom, Dad and Joey played miniature golf. Afterward, they went out for burgers and talked. Of everyone in the family, Joey seemed to understand roles the best. He could list off everyone's role very quickly, even his own role. Most people have a hard time considering their own roles. It seemed to Jerry and Janet that the younger the person, the more he or she relied upon and appreciated the fact that everyone had roles. However, as the children grew older, the roles seemed to blur more in their eyes and more selfishness seemed to make the conversations about the roles slower.

Jasmine's conversation was probably the biggest surprise to Jerry and Janet. They trusted she would see the truth, but they weren't sure how long it might to get through to her. This was one reason they decided to check Jasmine out of school. They thought they might need more time with her. So, Jerry got the afternoon off and planned to spend the day understanding Jasmine.

At first, Jasmine was shocked that her parents would check her out. She didn't really know how to take the event. It was a first for sure. Then, when they took her out to her favorite Mexican restaurant, she really thought something had to be up. "Had someone died?" she wondered.

After they started eating, Janet started the conversation by asking Jasmine what she wanted out of her relationship with them. This was too much for Jasmine. She exploded, "What are you guys doing? Why are we here? Why are you asking me funny questions? Are you trying to trick me or something? Do you want me to think you really care or some craziness like that?"

"Do you want us to care, Jaz?" Jerry responded in a loving and understanding tone. "Do you feel like we don't care? If so, why?"

After a few minutes of crying and getting her breaths under control, she unloaded her deep feelings on her parents. She told them that she had pretty much given up on the family and the idea of ever being close to her parents. She talked about how they didn't understand her, and how she just wanted them to care about her life and understand her. She said she felt trapped in their family because she didn't have anyone to talk to about all the stuff going on in her life and at home. She wanted to be free from all of it and from them.

At this point Janet talked to Jasmine about how they wanted her to have more freedom and happiness, and how they wanted to respect her more and wanted her to be able to respect them. Then through the conversation, which had become very open and honest, she understood roles and felt a sense of freedom from loneliness. In fact, she was so converted to the roles concept that she said, "Mom, I know I haven't respected your role. I've walked all over you. Dad, I've been really mean to you too. Sorry. I'm going to work on this."

This honest admission of wrongdoing was healing to Jaz and to her parents. There was definitely something to hope for now. This family really could change if Jaz could be that honest and change that quickly. Now they were ready to learn the next lesson from Sage.

When they arrived at Sage's house the following Monday evening, they were so excited to give a report about the dates they'd had, as well as the change that had occurred in each of their hearts from just having a better understanding of roles. Sage and Abi listened intently and smiled a lot at each other because they knew just what this new freedom felt like. They remembered it like it was yesterday.

"Well, Sage, that is our report. We feel like we've done a lot, but the family is still reacting to each other in negative ways — even though they've learned about roles. For a few days they treated each other differently, but they are pretty much back to their old ways of treating each other. Although, I will say they seem to be genuinely trying to be different sometimes," Jerry said.

"Well, it sounds like the Justice family has some habits to break," Sage assessed.

"Habits are interesting. They're kind of like snowflakes. They seem small and insignificant at first, but after they occur over and over again, like falling snowflakes, they become very destructive and hard to stop — kind of like an avalanche," added Abigail.

"That's exactly what it feels like," said Janet. "It's like we're trying to hold back the tide or stop an avalanche."

Janet took a deep breath and said, "Abigail, I've realized something. As we've talked to all the children about roles, I couldn't help but think about my role as a teacher. I haven't really been doing that well. I guess I bought into some popular ideas about parenting that have really made me think differently about who I am and who my children are. I remember someone named Dr. Benjamin Spock who promoted the idea that parents should be friends, not parents. I guess I always wanted my children to see me as their friend, so I've spent years trying to be as nice as possible and doing things to stop them from whining or getting angry. It seems to me now that I haven't really been teaching them that much. I guess I've pretty much failed as a parent, huh?"

"Not at all, Janet! I know what you're feeling. We wondered at one point if we had failed in our parent role too," Abigail responded lovingly.

She continued, "It's never too late to fix your roles in order to fix your relationships. God gave you a role as the teacher of your children. Every day you know and act on that principle is a day you're fulfilling a vital role God gave you to do. Don't get discouraged. Even living your role just one day is a day your children have you as a teacher. You have a lifetime of time. Don't worry about past mistakes or misunderstandings. I don't think Dr. Spock was completely wrong in his teachings. Parents and children should become the best of friends, but starting with friendship is where he misunderstood the goal. If a parent starts out by treating their child like a friend, then the roles will be confusing for the child. In no time the child will become a tyrant because appropriate boundaries and skills haven't been learned.

"When the roles are put in their proper places and parents teach and lead their children, and when children learn from and follow their parent's good example, then the family experiences deep unity. This unity promotes the most meaningful friendships possible. Our children are our best friends and always will be, but not because we wanted a friend from the start. They are our friends and confidants because we've all deliberately decided to live according to our roles when they were young, and now they have new roles as fathers and mothers of their own families."

"Thanks, Abigail," said Janet. "I guess I never thought of friendship as something that had to take roles into account. So now that I'm okay with being a teacher of my children, what do I do next? I don't really know how to live my assigned role, and I don't know how to hold back the tide of emotion at my house."

Abigail smiled. "Janet," she said, "you don't have to actually be perfect at your role before you live it. Just like an actor in a play pretends his or her role, you might need to deliberately pretend your role at first until it becomes natural. When it becomes natural, then you start thinking more like the character you desire to be. Just begin being the mother you know you're meant to be, even if you know you don't feel completely confident at that role yet. You can teach yourself your role, and while you work on that, we can teach you how to help stop the emotional tide at your house."

"I guess you're both ready for lesson two now," said Sage. "This lesson is probably the most painful of all the lessons. Roles are self-evident, so they were easy to see. But there are other things you need to be honest about in order to make the changes you want."

CHAPTER 9

LESSON TWO

For to be free is not merely to cast off one's chains, but to live in a way that respects and enhances the freedom of others.

Nelson Mandela

"Well, Sage, I don't really see any going back at this point. We've already had to admit that we had an identity problem. And we had to step out of our comfort zones to talk about it with each other and the children," said Jerry.

"Yes," said Sage, "But are you ready to give up your excuses? I guess we could call lesson two 'Giving Up Your Excuses.' In order to give up your excuses you need to do two things: First, you will need to analyze what kind of family you want to be and what things keep getting in the way of your family goal. Then you'll need to make a plan for how you will teach the children cause and effect. This plan will include boundaries your children will have to observe and consequences your children will have. This means you'll determine what things are distracting your family from your goals, and set limits for using or doing those things."

Jerry looked thoughtful as he questioned, "What do you mean we 'will need to analyze what kind of family' we want? Don't we already have a family?"

Sage smiled and said, "Jerry, I don't mean to confuse you. Let me explain. Of course you already have a family. What I mean is what do you want your family to feel like? What do you want your family culture to be like? Every family has its own culture. That is a key factor in how the children behave and experience life. What words do you and Janet want to use to describe your family? Or maybe you would like to think of a picture the family can keep in mind as a goal for the future. You could pick a holiday or special event that will happen 20 years from now — something that will have a special feeling associated with it. That united feeling will give the family a reason to care about the changes they're going to be making as a group."

"Oh, you're talking about making a vision with some specific vocabulary, huh? We tried to do this at work once, but no one really seemed to care much about the vision for the company. I don't know if it really worked," responded Jerry.

"You bring up a really good point," said Sage. "Visions are only good if the people who have the vision care about them and deliberately keep them in mind by practicing the feeling the vision is supposed to have each day. How about I share another vision with you that will help you understand why having a family vision is so important?"

Sage continued, "I don't know if you've ever studied the Anglo-Saxon people who were the founders of Angle land, which ended up becoming what we know as England. They had a very interesting form of government. It was based on freedom, roles, and problem solving. The base of their government structure was self-government.

"Here's how it worked. If a person had a problem, no matter what kind of problem, they went through the same procedure to solve it. Let's say a person lost his job and needed income. The first person he would go to for help would be himself. He would problem solve his own situation by determining what money he needed to provide for his family, what income he still could count on, and what skills he possessed that he could market for new employment or income.

"After this man exhausted all his own resources and analyzed the skills he possessed and needed, he would go about developing any necessary new skills. While he worked on his dream of being self-reliant by using his own skills, he would go to his next line of defense in crisis for help — his family.

"If possible, this man's family would help him financially or with skill development. If the family wasn't able to assist him with his needs, he would go to his next line of defense — his friends or community. The man's friends would help him network for a job and teach him what skills they felt he needed. They might also give him a loan or a gift of money to help him financially for a time.

"If the man wasn't able to get help from his friends, he would approach his church for help. The church would assist in keeping his family fed, and help him network for employment opportunities.

"Finally, if the church was unable to help the man, he would approach the government for assistance. The government would have the least amount of resources, but would have mercy on him if no one else was able to steer the man in the right direction," concluded Sage.

"I know this is basic for you, Sage, but in our society this model isn't followed. I guess it died with the Anglo-Saxons. Maybe it just wasn't realistic. Most people I know with problems, especially financial ones, go straight to the government for help," said Jerry.

Sage continued, "Jerry, this model of self-government didn't start with the Anglo-Saxons, and it didn't end with them either. The Anglo-Saxon people modeled their self-government structure after the Israelite people from the Old Testament in the Bible. In the Bible there's an account of Moses dividing the people into groups of 10 families, 50 families, 100 families, and so on. The Anglo-Saxons did the same thing. So, I guess the idea started in biblical times, but it has been present in recent times too.

"The founding Fathers of the United States read the history of the Anglo-Saxon people and saw their form of government as good.

They saw that the self-government structure of society led each individual to problem solve for themselves. Families were expected to instruct their children when they needed help problem solving. And then, if the family wasn't able to help the person, the rest of society was to get involved in the problems of one person.

"Here, maybe this will help." Sage took out his ever-present carpenter pencil from behind his ear and started drawing in his notebook. He drew five concentric circles and labeled them.

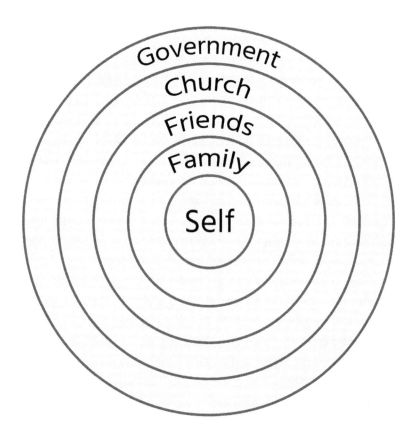

Janet blurted out, "I feel like a huge light bulb just went on, Sage!

You're saying our society was founded on self-government and problem solving, but for some reason we don't solve our own problems really well now. Why not? What has happened? So this model applies to not only financial problems, but to all problems."

"Janet, I see you're getting this," said Sage. "To answer your last question first: Yes, this model is for any problem. The self-government model was used for financial problems, behavioral problems, relationship problems, you name it.

"Now, let me answer your first question. What has happened to self-government and why don't people use their lines of defense in the proper order anymore? Well, the answer could vary for each individual, but for the sake of simplicity, this is what I see.

"People aren't as religious as they used to be, so they don't see church as a close contact they can call upon in trouble. Nowadays, friends are people we focus on impressing, but not necessarily being honest with. Because of pride and trying to appear to be something different than they are, people don't feel comfortable going to friends and community anymore. We're an image-based society now, and we don't want to look bad to our friends. Also, entitlement mentality discourages people from reaching out to their community of friends for help because the person in trouble might have to take responsibility and pay a friend back for the loan. They just don't want to look the person in the face after the loan. And finally, families are more dysfunctional than they've ever been. Dysfunction is the new function in our modern world. People have disconnected from family and don't see them as a friendly resource for help anymore. Plus, the people in a position to lead or help in a family are often misused and tired of helping people who don't use the help to better their circumstances.

"Let me be clear about dysfunction and function. To function is to act or do business according to your duty, your office or your role. To be dysfunctional is to not act according to what your role is. If a child talks down to a parent or refuses to be obedient, or a parent behaves irresponsibly or childish and doesn't care properly for a child, then that is dysfunction."

When Sage showed them an updated image, Jerry commented, "That's a pretty sad picture of society. You've crossed out three of the five options for how the person can find help. Well, at least the person still has themselves and the government."

Abigail looked at Sage with raised eyebrows and said, "Jerry, this isn't really the full story. You're right, there seems to be two options left, but actually the person in trouble nowadays doesn't trust himself to solve his own problem. He hasn't really learned how to problem solve and is also afraid of failure. So, the person wants an expert, not himself. Also, he's used to his problems being solved really fast, so he goes straight to the government because in his mind that's the fast, easy solution. It's instant relief. So, I guess we really should cross out half of the circle that says 'self' because the person really only sees himself as half a person and expects someone else to solve his problem for him.

"Also, many people nowadays have lost faith in the government.

They see the government as failing and slow to solve problems. They don't want to turn to the government because it usually goes against their principles. They want to maintain some of their pride. People in this circumstance end up very low. They're often very depressed and can even become suicidal."

Sage put his pencil to the page again.

"Well, Sage, this seems like a hopeless picture. I hope you're going to tell us there's something we can do, or I might as well go home and drown myself in chocolate," said Jerry.

Sage smiled and said, "There is hope. There is always hope, Jerry. I've actually already explained the solution to the global problem. The solution is the self-government model of problem solving. If parents are aware of this model and recognize their role in the structure, then the whole world can change in one generation. The diagram proves that the solution for happiness and freedom in the self-government system is that the 'self' must know how to problem solve. Each person must understand cause and effect and develop an ability to see what's right and what's wrong.

"Parents must teach children cause and effect from the very beginning by having positive and negative consequences for actions in their family government structure. Parents must also realize that the problem-solving part of a child's brain isn't fully developed until at least age 18, but sometimes later. Since this is the case, parents must keep teaching their children and correcting their children over and over again throughout the years of their youth.

"The Anglo-Saxon self-government plan for their nation is the grand plan for how to raise children into self-governing adults and how to solve the problems in society. The parents are to teach their children self-government, and then the children who have minimal problems will be problem-solving leaders in their nation. Does this make sense?" Sage asked as he turned the paper toward them to reveal another image.

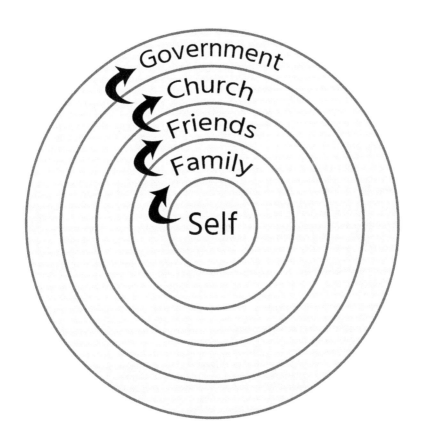

"Sage, this makes so much sense," said Jerry. "In fact, my mind is all over the place right now. This one picture has explained so many problems in our society and what the solution must be. No piece of government legislation is going to fix our world. Only the people, with their power to transform themselves, hold the power to set things right again. I want those children. How do I do it? They won't even follow a simple instruction from us sometimes," explained Jerry.

"Just a minute," said Sage as he stood up and headed for his study. A moment later he returned holding a small box. Handing the box to Jerry, Sage said, "Open it. It's one of my treasures."

Inside the box was a small, old-fashioned scale that might have been used for measuring small amounts of things like medicines or powders. Looking up, Jerry said, "I'm not sure I understand, Sage."

Sage pondered and then asked, "You've read 'The Merchant of Venice' by William Shakespeare?"

"Yes," said Janet. "I've always liked that play. I know what you're saying now. You're saying that we need to make sure our economy has justice and mercy, huh?"

"That's right, Janet," said Sage. "This small scale was given to me by my father when I was married to remind me that my role as a husband and father needed to involve justice and mercy. Your last name is Justice. You probably really understand that word, but what about mercy?"

"That's the irony, Sage," said Jerry. "We're the Justice family, but we haven't really had an environment of justice at all. I don't think we correct the children that often because we're afraid of an emotional power struggle. I guess knowing our role would really have helped this problem.

"And about mercy... as I understand mercy, a person can't actually show mercy unless justice exists at first. Yikes! This means that at the Justice house we've been letting the kids walk all over us, but haven't shown them justice or mercy in the process. I think we thought we were being kind and merciful. Oh, what a realization!" exclaimed Jerry.

CHAPTER 10

SOME STRUCTURE

Even if the parent doesn't always tell the child what he wants to hear, in the end the parent is more respected for having values and structure.

Nicholeen Peck, Parenting A House United

"Let's sum up what we've talked about thus far," said Sage as Abigail passed out glasses of lemonade to everyone. "You need to decide what kind of family you want to have, and maybe even create a deliberate picture in your minds that takes place 20 years from now so that the goal is a real vision. As part of your vision for your family, you need to know the family's role in society and government, and understand the importance of the family. The family is the most powerful or destructive institution in the world. You need a system, or economy in your home, that teaches cause and effect. You also need a problem solving system, and if this system is going to change the hearts of you and your family, then it must be based on the principles of justice and mercy. And finally, all this will lead to self-government, which is the individual power we all have to solve any problem."

Jerry looked a little distraught as he said, "Sage, I don't mean to sound dumb, but how are we going to set up this family economy you talk about that sounds so principled when our family seems so out of control?"

"Remember, Jerry, the solutions to your family problems are not in one quick fix. There's a process your family is going to have to go through to make the changes you desire. So far we've talked about recognizing roles and the power roles have in all relationships, and today we've talked about analyzing your family. Analyze what you want for your family and what's really happening in your family. The next step, what we're talking about right now, is making a plan to accomplish the desired vision. Step one, recognize roles; step two, analyze; and step three, plan."

"That's definitely what we need, a plan," said Janet.

"There are three parts to a good family plan," said Sage after sipping from his glass of lemonade. "First, the economy; second, no excuses; and third, family standards.

"Each family needs to have a system of credits and debits, or you might call them positive and negative consequences, as part of their family economy. Positive consequences teach the child that his decision was right and is often simple, like a high five or words of affirmation — although the consequences can be tangible. The negative consequences should also be simple.

"One of my favorite authors is Samuel Smiles, a nineteenth century author who wrote a book called 'Character.' His book says, 'Work is the antidote for a sick character.' When a child won't follow instructions from parents, their character is sick. That's why our family uses work as the negative consequence to most attitude problems or behavioral issues."

Janet, looking concerned, said, "I don't mean to be a naysayer, but our kids won't lift a finger even when they're going to get an allowance out of it. I don't know if work will be effective for our family economy."

"Don't worry," answered Sage. "It's possible to use work as a negative consequence because the child is never allowed to do their extra chore until they're calm and have accepted the consequence. They have to *willingly* do the job. That is the only way for them to take complete ownership of their own behaviors. So, you will not allow the chore to be done until the child is calm and has accepted the correction and the consequence willingly."

"That sounds too good to be true, Sage," said Jerry doubtfully.

"I know, just stick with me, Jerry. It really works," assured Sage. "A person can never learn self-government if they're not allowed to calmly accept a negative consequence. So, don't plan on making your children work when they're angry. They will be calm before you ever get to that point. For that calmness to occur, you may have to learn what Abigail and I call 'The Rule of Three,' which is a series of instructions that have three other consequences attached to them if the child is unable to follow instructions."

"What do you mean 'follow instructions?' Is that so hard? Wait. What am I saying? My kids already don't follow instructions, I guess. So, okay. Keep going," said Jerry.

"Jerry," said Sage. "I'm not going to teach you the five steps to following instructions right now. I'll give you a book to help with learning that skill, as well as some other instructional materials you'll need to help you. For now, just think of yourself coming up with an economy. After some good analysis, both of you will plan your family vision, and then you'll start your plan by deciding what positive and negative consequences your family wants. I caution you against issuing a 'loss of privileges' for each little thing because that's something you take away. With a loss of privileges, they don't get the opportunity to demonstrate immediate acceptance of the consequence by doing something like a chore."

"Okay. I think we can come up with an economy and incorporate justice and mercy. Now, what about that second thing you said: 'No excuses'?" Jerry asked.

Sage smiled. "This will be the hardest part of your plan. For years you've given the children excuses to use against you, and you've given them excuses. Your whole family has been living a lie. And, sadly, you've built communication habits around those lies."

"I don't think we lie that much," said Jerry, somewhat defensively. "We've always tried to be honest, Sage."

Abigail cut in. "Oh, we know you're honest people, but you've been lying to yourselves and your family for a long time. We all fall into that trap sometimes. The task is to pull ourselves out of the lie and take responsibility for our own actions and feelings. When you coddle the children, you have an excuse in your mind why you do that. When you get angry at each other, the children or your boss, you make an excuse or a justification for why you're entitled to lose control. Your children do the same thing. They talk disrespectfully to you and feel justified. Or they're cruel to each other and blame the other person for their sadness. When a person is a leader, when that's their role, they don't make excuses for how they feel or how they react. Instead, they take ownership and fix problems."

"I'm thinking back to something you said when we first started talking about this new lesson. You said it would hurt. This is the painful part, isn't it?" asked Janet.

Abigail lovingly responded, "Yes. This is a really painful part of learning your own self-government. You see, you can't teach your children to stop their bad behaviors and learn self-government if you're not also willing to do the same for your bad behaviors. The lie would undermine your teaching. Of course, it's also painful to plan consequences and decide to consistently follow through on your teaching."

"How do we stop making excuses? Is there a method for this?" Jerry inquired.

"Yes," said Sage. "You can plan a skill set for anything you want to change about yourself. Let's do some analysis. When do you make the excuses?"

"After we do something we shouldn't, I guess," said Jerry.

"That's right," said Sage. "But you also make excuses before you make a bad choice. Have you noticed that? You wouldn't make a bad choice or communicate wrongly if you didn't tell yourself it was okay. So, you need to recognize what happens right before you justify your upcoming bad actions."

"That's easy for me," said Janet. "I feel stressed. I always lose it when I'm stressed. Then I feel guilty because I know I messed up. I guess I also give in to the kids when I'm stressed too. I tell myself I can't take anymore conflict, so I give up."

"Fabulous analysis, Janet!" said Abigail. "That's how it happens with me too. This is how I made a change in me. I decided to deliberately notice what my body felt like right before making a bad choice to give up, or to give into a power struggle. After I knew what feeling to look for, I asked God to help me always recognize this feeling. Then, when I felt the feeling of stress coming, on I tell myself to stop talking, get calm, and think clearly. Even if I have to take a few extra minutes before I respond to a situation, it's worth it if I am ready to do what I plan to do — instead of reverting to my destructive default habit."

I'm going to try that!" said Janet. "I had no idea there was anything I could do to change me. I thought I was just the way I was and everyone, including me, would have to just deal with it. Oh, I'm already feeling freedom and I haven't even stopped my bad habits yet. But, if you can, I'm going to as well."

"What is the third thing we need to do? You said before we needed standards, right?" asked Jerry.

"Right," said Sage. "As part of your planning stage, you and Janet need to sit down and decide what standards your family will have about language, clothing, food, drugs, hair styles, tattoos, music, books, movies, computers, iPods, iPads, phones, gaming, etc. Besides laziness, the main reason parents end up in conflict with their teenage children is because the parents and children don't agree on the standards the child is supposed to live by. I hear parents complain about their children being on computer games and phones too much, but they still keep letting the child live that standard. Why? Most likely because they feel like it would be too much of a fight to change the standard now."

"You're so right, Sage!" said Jerry. "That's exactly where we're at in our family. We hate the disconnection that's happening, but don't really know how to shut off the devices and reconnect the family without a huge fight. And we want to preserve our family relationships a little bit."

"Let's look at your relationships," said Sage. "If they're disconnected from you, are your relationships good? No. So, it can't hurt your relationships to remove the devices. Don't worry. You aren't going to implement the standard this week. I will talk you through that later, but you must make a standard. This standard makes it so your family doesn't need to talk about all the issues on the document that much. The document backs you up when you have to tell the children 'no' or instruct them to do something they might not want to do. Abigail and I sat down one night years ago and wrote down anything and everything we could think of that would be a standard we would have to decide between. We even tried to look ahead to what new fads or problems could occur as our children grew older and were at risk to be exposed to immorality and distractions."

"Wow!" exclaimed Jerry. "I never thought of just deliberately sitting down and planning what our family would and wouldn't do, would and wouldn't say, would and wouldn't wear, would and wouldn't drink, etc. This is so proactive. I think writing all this down will also improve my confidence when I have to tell our children 'no' about something related to a standard because I won't feel like each new standard is a new issue right then, when we're in the moment. I love this! It's so deliberate!"

Sage and Abigail smiled at each other. "We know exactly what you mean. Acting deliberately is the key to preparing for problems before they happen so that you don't have to emotionally react to the problems in the moment," said Abigail.

Sage added, "I think we've probably given you enough to work on tonight. If you analyze your family relationships, make a family vision, a family economy and a family standard, as well as stop any excuses, you'll have a full week. Do you want to come back and let us know how it goes in a week? Keep in mind you won't be able to change the behaviors completely yet. Don't even share the economy, the standard or the vision with the children yet. Let's wait for a week, but in the meantime you can talk about not living a lie, and you can help the family to stop making excuses."

"It's going to be so hard to make a vision and an economy, and not share it with the kids," said Jerry.

"I know," said Sage. "But you'll want to have all three lessons before you can start conquering all the negative behaviors at home. So, start by deliberately self-governing yourselves, and just wait for one week."

~ CHAPTER 11 ~

PLANNING MORE THAN HOME LIFE

Jerry and Janet went on a special date and did a lot of family planning. They made a list of the problems they saw in their relationships. They also made a list of the lies associated with those problems.

Problem	Lie
Being short-tempered with each other	Someone is trying to bother me or doesn't care about me.
Boredom	Someone else needs to entertain me.
Using digital devices too much	We have to stay connected online
Laziness	We don't have time to work
Not talking to each other	We don't have a lot in common
Bad attitudes and selfishness	Others try to oppress me or no one understands me
Yelling and whining	If I don't apply force to the situation, nothing will change

Then they made a list of the words they wanted to be part of their family vision, while at the same time keeping in mind what they wanted their family to become.

United
Loving
Supportive
Learning
Leaders
Friends
Happiness
Freedom
Trusting
Faith
Deliberate
Fun
Self-Governed
Respectful

After some careful analysis Janet and Jerry wrote out a beautiful family vision. They developed a story of 20 years in the future at a family Christmas party. At this party the family would feel united and be genuine, best friends. They would have open, honest communication, and they would feel love and comfort when they were together. This story was filled with details too. They added the sounds of Christmas, the smells of Christmas, and the fun family traditions of Christmas. They deliberately decided that they would practice the feeling of the family Christmas 20 years in the future every time they were together as a family, but especially every Christmas.

The family vision plan led to the plan for the family standard. They knew in order to create a home like the one they could feel in their vision, they needed to change their family culture pretty drastically by incorporating deliberate standards.

They listed things like what kinds of words they would say and wouldn't say, what their family policy was on tattoos and piercings, as well as the policies on drugs, alcohol, sexual activities, and grooming and modesty standards. They were especially careful to define proper media usage. Since the family had an obvious addiction to devices, they needed to change the roles of the devices in their home, which included family entertainment, play toys and time fillers. Now the devices were going to be given their proper role as adult tools. The children would not be allowed to use a device of their own unless it was proven they were really good at self-governing. They also outlined important media boundaries, like never using a computer in a room alone and never using a device in bed.

Following the creation of the family standard, Jerry and Janet created a Justice family economy. They took Sage's advice and decided upon extra chores for negative consequences; and praise, high fives and hugs for the most commonly used positive consequences. They also talked about abandoning the negative and positive consequences they were currently using that revolved around media time. They had determined those media consequences created an entitlement mentality about the devices and almost gave the electronics too much attention in the home.

Janet and Jerry really loved learning about roles, analyzing, and planning for their goals. In fact, the three keys of self-government they had learned so far seemed to make all their relationships look different.

At Rickman Brother's, Jerry saw his position in a new light. He saw his role and respected it by following through with what he was responsible for by having a good attitude and working hard to meet his deadlines. His integrity improved. He couldn't help but deliberately analyze himself and his words at the office and with clients. His new appreciation for roles and for himself led him to value other people more and become less emotional about office politics. He even helped his department make a plan to create a more motivating work environment.

The big idea he presented was his biggest personal revelation from his home life: no more excuses.

"Jerry, I can't believe how everyone is so changed lately just because we all decided not to make excuses for our own emotions," said Cash on Friday afternoon. "I never thought I would see the day when office politics built people up and led to personal power instead of personal bondage. Honestly, I never knew we were in bondage. This week has been amazing! And one more thing I really appreciate you telling me about roles. I talked to my daughter about her role, my role and her mother's role — and there seems to be less frustration at our house. We aren't perfect or anything, but we have had an eye-opening experience."

"Thanks, Cash," said Jerry. "It's so fun to have someone to talk to about all the stuff I'm learning. I think I had to hit rock bottom in all my relationships to finally be ready to take ownership of my own behaviors. I feel so free. It makes we wonder if all World War II vets understood this kind of freedom. It boggles my mind that we've lost these basic principles so quickly. Why do you think our society got so messed up?"

"Jerry, the only thing I've been able to come up with on that one is 'stuff.' We have too much stuff. Too much prosperity and convenience. We just don't have to work as much as we used to, so we put on airs and start thinking about stuff more than about people. I know it sounds simplistic, but what other solution is there?" asked Cash.

"None, I guess," said Jerry. "You're probably right. Does that mean we need to get rid of our stuff and live off the land again? Is that the only way families worldwide will pull their lines of defense and roles back into line?"

"No, Jerry," responded Cash. "It just means we need to never forget about the self-government structure that freedom is based on. As soon as we start looking to someone else to solve our problems, we're in bondage again. I think it's easy to fall in that trap."

"Yeah, you're right," admitted Jerry. "I always find myself trying to think of a lazier way to do things. It's like my brain is addicted to finding a way to do less. I have to overcome that and find joy in working, just like my children need to learn to do."

CHAPTER 12

LESSON THREE

If parenting is about punishments, then parenting is only a battle for control. Our real responsibility as parents is to communicate a reason for a change of heart in our children.

Nicholeen Peck, Parenting A House United

66 **T**hanks for letting us come back over, Sage," said Jerry. "We've really loved the mentoring you and Abigail have given us. Our lives will never be the same. You said there were three lessons and that until we do lesson three the problems won't go away. We're already seeing improvement just by changing our own hearts and understanding more about self-government, but we really want to have the family problems go away now. What's lesson three?"

"First, I have to say that Abigail and I are impressed. You both are so motivated and have been so good by following through with every instruction we've given you. You're acting deliberately, and it shows. That brings me to lesson three. You've already done the first of the five keys of self-government: roles, analyze and plan. Today we're going to talk about how to apply the final two keys: act deliberately and communicate effectively," said Sage.

"Lucky for you," said Abigail. "You've already been acting deliberately. You talked to your children about roles and reported back.

Then you analyzed, planned, stopped making excuses, and checked back with us. You're acting deliberately. Deliberate action is the most powerful part of learning self-government. It makes all the difference in your teaching, correcting, and in your home culture."

"The last time you and Sage talked about being deliberate, it really made an impression on me," Janet said. "Throughout the whole week I kept thinking, 'I'm the leader, and a leader acts deliberately — not reactively.' I feel like 'deliberate' means that I have a plan; that I have thought things out before I do them.'"

"That makes me think of one of my favorite leadership books, 'The 7 Habits of Highly Effective People' by Stephen Covey. But in that book I think he calls the concept 'being proactive,'" added Jerry.

"Jerry, I think being proactive is just part of being deliberate," countered Janet. "A deliberate person is proactive and makes plans, but a deliberate person also does something different because they have a plan."

"Wow, you two!" exclaimed Sage. "You really seem to be getting into this. How about Abigail tells you how to do lesson three now? You are definitely ready for it. I love seeing all the fireworks go off as you put the pieces of teaching yourselves and your family self-government together." Sage smiled and pulled his chair closer to Abigail. "Go ahead, honey. You're great at teaching about deliberate action. I should know, I learned it from you."

"No you didn't. I learned it from you. You had a hard time when you returned home from the war. The year in the German prison camp really took its toll on you. You could have given up, but you didn't. You deliberately kept going. When I saw you deliberately keep living your role even though it was painful for you, I knew I could deliberately do *anything*," Abigail said with tears in her eyes.

"Abi, you were the inspiring one when I got home from the war. You stuck with me when I had a lot of healing to do. You put up with my crazy thoughts and bad dreams. You loved me when I was hard to love. And what's more, you deliberately carried on and cared for the family all alone when I wasn't here for almost three years. I've always admired you for your strength. I even leaned on your strength from time to time. You're the most deliberate person I know. In fact, I don't think we would have done half as well with our family if it wouldn't have been for you deliberately making family dinners. You also helped our family by deliberately making fun family projects and learning activities for us," Sage said as he looked into his wife's once bright blue, but now graying, eyes.

Jerry and Janet speechlessly exchanged glances and smiled. It was obvious that Abigail and Olton Sage were desperately and deeply in love with each other, even though their youth had faded. "I want to be like the Sage's when we grow old," thought Jerry as he winked at Janet and squeezed her hand.

Silence permeated the room and lasted for about 30 seconds. The moment seemed too special to ruin with words. Finally, Abigail spoke. "Sorry, Janet. Sorry, Jerry. I guess these talks with you are pretty inspiring for us too. Whenever a person speaks the truth, it draws her closer to the people she loves."

"Where were we? Oh yes, acting deliberately and communicating effectively," Abigail said with a cheerful voice. "You both seem to be understanding the principle of acting deliberately. You're both right; it's planning ahead — which is something we call 'pre-preteaching.' Preteaching is doing the teaching before there's a problem to solve. You have both spent a lot of time laying the foundational work for a family culture shift at your home. Now it's time to put that plan into action."

Sage quickly added, "Remember last week when I said we would give you a book to help you? Well, here it is. The book is called, 'Parenting: A House United.' We're just going to call this an early Christmas present, okay?"

Janet and Jerry smiled, and their eyes twinkled. "Okay. You didn't need to do this. Thank you so much!" Janet said.

Sage looked at Abigail and lifted his eyebrows. "Well, actually we did need to get the book for you. You see, lesson three is the most complicated of all the lessons and takes the most time. We know you'll have questions, and that you'll want to keep learning about how your family can act deliberately and communicate effectively. After reading this book, we decided to get copies for all our family members. It puts into words why we were having parenting problems and provides skills to help us be a happy, united family. Sure, we knew a lot of stuff, but our life experiences didn't completely prepare us for the hardest role we would ever have, that of being a parent."

"Right you are," said Abigail. "Parenting is hard stuff, which is why deliberate parents make deliberate plans and teach deliberate skills. That book that my husband just handed you teaches four skills that every child needs to know, and the five skills that every adult needs to know. It also talks about three types of meetings a self-governing family uses to see how well the family is doing on the family relationships, the family vision, and family's self-governing."

Turning to Jerry and Janet, Abigail said, "When Olton and I started trying to fix our relationships with our children, we knew we had to change the words we were saying to them. This meant we needed to change how we described what was going wrong and what was going right. We also needed to prepare our whole family by teaching the children a common vocabulary that we could all have to describe behaviors, our family culture, and our relationships."

"Tell them about the skills, Abi," said Sage with excitement.

"As you can see, Olton loves the skills in this book and can't wait for you to have them," Abigail said as she winked at her husband.

"You see, without skill sets we wouldn't have been able to give our family the vocabulary shift we needed in order to break old, destructive habits. The skills the children need, as well as the skills the parents need, for self-government are the biggest piece of lesson three. When your family learns these skills, you'll be able to act more deliberately as a family, and you'll communicate more effectively."

"You know, there's a big difference between communicating effectively and communicating efficiently. Effective communication often takes more time and requires a deep connection. Efficient communication is often the type of communication that is meant to be quick. People say as few words as possible to finish the interaction quickly. Effective communication is well thought out and delivered deliberately. It's always better to communicate with a deliberate plan than to try to communicate quickly."

Jerry looked concerned. "Are you saying that to do lesson three I'm going to have get used to talking more? I'm not a real talker. Historically, I've tried to just give a look — or not give any looks at all — to try to handle problems at home."

Sage smiled and said, "Jerry, I know what you mean. By my nature, I'm not much of a talk-it-out-type of guy either. But after deciding to communicate more effectively, my relationships changed so much I couldn't go back. Besides, I learned that sometimes I was actually saying too much when I was not communicating effectively. I would lecture until I thought the child got my point. Lectures are not effective communication. So, some parents are more effective when they talk less, and others are more effective when they talk more. I had to do a combination of both. It was really about remembering what's called the Five Teaching Styles and the Four Basic Skills."

"The what? I'm lost," admitted Janet.

"You aren't lost, Janet. This is just the perfect time to talk to you about the skills you'll find in the book and how to correct the problems you'll encounter," Abigail said. "Don't worry. We'll make sure you know what you're doing.

"Now, there's a lot in that book," continued Abigail. "We can't possibly tell you all of it, so be sure to read it, and discuss it together as you implement the skills. Since you have a lot of behaviors to fix, you might want to start with the third section of the book. Work on the skills in that section and then do sections one and two.

"There are six steps you'll take when you go home. First, read the book, starting with the third section. Second, practice the Four Basic Skills and Five Teaching Styles together so that you begin feeling confident. Role play may feel silly sometimes. But they are nothing more than very deliberate preparation for future, positive interactions. And remember, it's impossible to live the role you know you should be living without deliberately working on the skills you need in your role.

"Third, after you role play the parent and child skills as a couple, then gather your family together to have a talk about your family vision. Talk to them about what you want for your family, and ask them if they would like to add anything to the Christmas picture you've created for your family. Following the family adoption of your family vision, the family should be ready to talk about how you'll all achieve your family vision. The vision is the reason the family will care about making changes, and the skills and deliberate communications will be how the family makes the changes to fit the vision.

"Fourth, the family needs to learn and role play the skills. The Four Basic Skills mentioned in the book are how to follow an instruction, accept 'no' answers and criticism, accept consequences, and how to disagree appropriately. Learning these four skills corrects 99.9% of all behavior problems in people.

"Naturally, after you teach the Four Basic Skills, the children will need to learn about the parent skills. You'll need to teach the children the Five Teaching Styles you'll use as parents to help teach them, correct problems, and help them be calm when they feel out of control. Role play these too; sometimes even switching roles during the role plays. When they know exactly how you will respond to any situation, even knowing what words you are likely to say, they will be less anxious and see you as the examples of self-government. Less anxiety and more predictability creates confident, self-governing children. No emotional reactions will even seem necessary after your family feels the freedom of deliberate, pre-planned family problem solving."

"Okay, I'm ready to try anything Abigail, but I'm still not so sure my children will try it. Aren't they kind of old to be trying new tricks? I guess I'm having a bit of doubt right now. I can see how teaching a small child how to follow instructions or disagree appropriately would be really easy to do, but to teach this to an 18-year-old son seems impossible," Janet confessed.

"Freedom," Jerry whispered as he squeezed Janet's hand. "No excuses, remember? We can do this. What do we have to lose? They already don't want to change."

"Right. You see what a habit excuse-making is for me. You're right. That's the hardest part. I'm obviously not done with lesson two," Janet said with a sigh.

"No one is ever done with lesson two," said Sage. "We all have habits of thought that we have to stop. The thought habits manifest themselves as excuses for most people. You're ready to move on with lesson three. Just keep mentoring each other along. That's what Abi and I have been doing for most of our lives now. It's a sign of trust in your relationship too. One of the roles of a husband or wife is to be a mentor. We're all strong in different ways, so we must allow our spouses to mentor us. Oh, and about this only being for little children — it's actually for all ages. I'm still trying to master self-government for myself. The skills are for life. We taught these skills to some of our children when they were in their teen years, and they responded well. Of course, it's easier to learn self-government when you're younger, but no one is ever too old."

"Okay, Sage. I'm just going to trust you and Abigail on this," Janet said hopefully.

"I can only give you assurance that it will work, Janet. That's what a mentor does. After the assurance comes the turning point called 'deliberate action.' Only after you take deliberate action can the evidence come. So, now is the moment of courage. Now you need to study a bit more about the vital skills you'll need to get the vision and feeling you want in your home culture. Then, you'll need to deliberately teach them to your family," explained Abigail.

"Fifth, when you're teaching your family the way you'll correct the problem by using the Five Teaching Styles, then you'll acquaint them with the family economy you've established," continued Abigail. "Then, after a week or so of practicing the skills and correcting the problems in a loving, effective way, you'll be ready to have the three meetings the book teaches you how to have.

"Sixth, the family will be ready to adopt the family standard in a family meeting. A family standard is a family document that lists rules about language, media, grooming, health, friends, etc. The family standard stops lots of family contention by becoming the source of the instructions and 'no' answers that are usually most difficult to accept, such as no revealing clothing and no digital devices allowed in bedrooms at night. The book contains specific instructions about how to adopt the standards in a calm way.

"Mr. and Mrs. Justice, do you have those six steps down?" Abigail inquired.

Jerry wanted to check his memory first. "Let me see: first, read the book; second, practice the skills as a couple; third, talk about vision with the family; fourth, teach the family the Four Basic Skills; fifth, teach the family the Five Teaching Styles and family economy; and sixth, adopt the family standard. How did I do? Did I get them all?"

"Impressive, honey!" said Janet with a nudge. "But I think we better put this to-do list on paper. I don't want to miss anything important."

Sage sat up straight with a new idea. "Oh, before we set you off on this new parenting journey, I think it's important to let you know what to expect. It doesn't always go smooth right at first. We're all pretty attached to our old, unhealthy habits and lies. Even when we see the truth of how things should be, it can be hard to make the changes right in the minute. This goes for you and the children. Your children will likely test you a bit before choosing to self-govern. And you'll both likely have moments when you go back to old habits too. A deliberate person doesn't stop when a setback occurs. A deliberate person starts the interaction over. In our family we call the moments when we need to reset an 'interaction' or a 'start again re-dos.' When you make a mistake, because you will from time to time, just stop and say, 'Excuse me, that wasn't good self-government. I'm going to re-do that.'"

"Thank you for that bit of a reality check, Sage," said Jerry. "I'm kind of an idealist and could be in danger of giving up if I see things not going right. We have to deliberately prepare to restart when things go off track. I like that. I'm beginning to see that learning self-government has everything to do with being deliberate. This is really liberating."

"And scary," added Janet. "I've had a habit of allowing myself to be emotionally walked on for many years now, so it's exciting and scary to start interacting with the children more deliberately and less emotionally."

CHAPTER 13

LIBERATION

When there is no enemy within, the enemies outside cannot hurt you.

Winston S. Churchill

"What a day," sighed Janet as she sat down next to Jerry on the sofa. The house was quiet, and finally they could talk alone about how the end of the first week of trying to communicate effectively was going.

"I feel like things are going pretty well, but I have never talked so much in a day to the children," admitted Jerry. "And now it's every day."

"I know what you mean," agreed Janet. "To think I've been parenting for over 18 years, and I had never thought of connecting with my children before I correct them. Connecting helps so they can not only have a change of heart but also a change in behavior."

"I used to only focus on what they did wrong," Jerry added. "I was so negative. Now, as part of the correction skills we learned from the book, 'Parenting: A House United,' I'm telling them what they should have done; and we're also practicing behaviors and calmness the right way. This new way of effective communication is so logical; it even feels like common sense. It's so liberating."

"Yes, and tiring," said Janet. "I don't think I'm used to thinking and acting so deliberately at home. It takes constant focus. Remember yesterday when Jasmine refused to get calm when I gave her a 'no' answer for using her phone during dinner? Sage was right when he said that things wouldn't be perfect at first. We've had our struggles while implementing this new way of effective communication."

"Who could forget that blow up at dinner?" asked Jerry. "I've never seen Jasmine get so upset in my life. She was screaming and hitting the table out of frustration from receiving the 'no' answer. I wasn't sure we were doing the right thing by being so deliberate when you started correcting Jasmine's tantrum. I actually remember thinking, 'Pick your battles, Janet.' Can you believe I thought that? Suddenly I was hoping you would back down so that we could just have some peace and quiet during dinner. In the end she did get calm, and the whole evening changed."

"Well, I used the Rule of Three that is explained in the book," replied Janet. "At first I didn't want to use that teaching style because it meant I would have to potentially give such large consequences and then actually have to follow through with them. I've never been great at follow through, but I made myself a promise that even I could follow through on the most important thing in my life — my family relationships.

"On day two I let Melissa and Joey ruin another morning by arguing over who's turn it was to let the dog out before I decided I would quickly use corrections and the Rule of Three. The children learned they had to keep themselves calm. Now they know if they don't keep themselves calm, I will need to help them.

"The Rule of Three is all about helping children remember the skill of how to get calm so that they can be understood. Our children, maybe even our whole family, had completely neglected that skill for so long that it's going to take consistently correcting the problem to make a new calm communication habit. The children can disagree appropriately, even with each other. They just need to keep themselves calm so that they can remember to use the skills they know now," said

Janet.

"I love that they have the skills for disagreeing appropriately!" Jerry said. "The other day Mark wanted to take my car again because his was out of gas. Of course I told him, 'No,' because he needs to learn responsibility. Then the unexpected happened. Mark said, 'Dad, I'm going to disagree appropriately, okay?' I tried not to look shocked, but I'm sure my face showed my surprise. I said he could.

"He went on to say, 'Dad, I know you want me to be responsible for myself and that's why you don't want me to use your car. But I need your car so that I can go get some money out of the bank before they close. I'm hoping to withdraw some money to fill my car and pay you back for the gas I used the other day. Would that be okay?' I almost cried, Janet. It was such an unselfish, grown-up disagreement. I felt like I finally saw him for who he was instead of through this ugly selfishness lens I've been viewing him through for a while now."

"Yes, Jerry. We are liberated. Now we just have to keep our freedom. I have a feeling it will be easy to fall back into old habits," Janet agreed. "Just this morning I found myself putting up with Joey's usual breakfast whining. The best part of my day happened when I governed myself by saying, 'Joey, I'm sorry. I'm not governing myself really well right now. I shouldn't be allowing you to whine at me. I'm going to start this again. Just now I told you that we are having poached eggs for breakfast, and you said, "Mom, you know I hate that." What you should have said was, "Okay." Or you could have disagreed appropriately. Since you chose not to do either, you have earned an extra chore.' To my shock, he said, 'Okay,' did his chore, practiced some role plays, and even ate the poached egg without dying."

Jerry chuckled and said, "Janet, our family will never be the same again. We know who we are. We know our roles. We know how to problem solve as a family. We have a plan. And we know we can act deliberately. Our home feels so different now. I know we aren't perfect yet. We're correcting and praising and problem solving all day long.

It's a lot more talking, but I think it will make it so that over time we actually have to talk about problems less. I see we are already getting it. I finally feel like I'm the father God meant me to be. I was trying to be a great father by playing a victim or dictator role. That wasn't who I was meant to be. My newly understood father role is infusing my life with happiness.

"I'm even disagreeing appropriately and saying, "Okay," at work. I'm different in the office, and people are noticing. I'm happy, Janet. My boss smiles at me, and people seem to have more confidence in me. The other day I had an entire meeting with Lance about my newfound mission to get the message out about roles where possible in the advertising we create. Cash and Lance see the importance of roles now and want to help me incorporate roles into as many campaigns as possible. We know we can strengthen the roles in families and society a bit by integrating proper roles in advertisements. The workday flies by. I love work again.

"Here's the craziest thing about me at work. The other day in the lunchroom some of the guys were talking about Lance in a bad way, and I did a correction. I said, 'Guys, right now you're talking about Lance in a negative way. It just makes the air thick at work, and no one ends up feeling comfortable, even us. If we have a problem, what we really should do is honor Lance's role by talking to him and disagreeing with him in an appropriate way.' They immediately stopped talking and then apologized and acknowledged that they really should just go talk to him. I corrected the guys at work because I knew the skills and principles behind how to do a proper correction. I never thought I would be able to correct another adult. I just gave the principles a try, and they worked," Jerry explained.

"Jerry, the self-government through effective communication has affected more than just our family. Melissa disagreed appropriately about the C grade she received on her paper because she misunderstood the assignment. The teacher granted her a second chance. Joey accepted a 'no' answer when the teacher at church told him he couldn't have his iPad out in class. I've corrected other people's children when they broke rules at our house. Oh, and our children seem to be inviting their friends over instead of playing electronics by themselves all the time. I gave them 'no' answers about their electronics for a while, and we're suddenly social again. The excuses and habits that once controlled us don't seem to even be an option anymore." Smiling, Janet added, "Sure, I know we'll have hard times, but we really are living that family vision more every day."

Jerry leaned back and put his arm around his wife as he said, "Yes, what a day. What a week. What a life we will have. We absolutely must invite Sage and Abigail over for our Christmas party this year. It will be a great family vision practice and celebration party for the new and improved Justice family. I don't know if we can ever thank them enough. The Bible says, 'The truth shall make you free.' That has certainly been true for the whole Justice family. The Sages have given us so much truth about ourselves and our families. I never knew this kind of liberation was possible."

Janet looked into her husband's eyes with the kind of love that can only come by sharing the same heart. Finally, they were on the same page about the family and about life. The world looked brighter, and her heart was somehow larger. She leaned toward her husband and gave him a kiss that said, "You are my perfect match. Thank you for all you have done to make my life wonderful."

CHAPTER 14

THE POWER OF IDENTITY

This above all: to thine ownself be true. And it must follow, as the night the day, Thou canst not then be false to any man.

William Shakespeare

"That was the best ham I've ever had!" Sage said to Jerry over dinner. "Thanks so much for the Christmas party and the great food."

"Sage, Abigail, this is not just a fun, holiday dinner together; it's our family vision, and it's our way of thanking you for changing our lives. The Justice family will never be the same again," Jerry shared.

"Yeah, we actually like each other now. I never thought I would see that day," said Jasmine.

"I don't remember how long it has been since I've been hit," Melissa confessed honestly.

Joey looked kind of shy for a minute and then added, "I actually play with my family now. I didn't used to do that."

Mark's girlfriend, Sarah, who was a little bit surprised at the honest communication, said, "Well, I hope my family can be this close one day. I didn't have that growing up, but I hope I can create that kind of family for my future children."

Mark looked right at Sarah and said with conviction, "My family is for sure going to be like this. I'm going to teach my family about roles, self-government, about who they really are, and about how important a family really is. I see how important it really is now. Thanks, Mom. Thanks, Dad. Thanks for being heroes in my life. I know we only recently made these changes, but they have significantly changed me. I didn't used to think I wanted marriage or a family. I thought they were nothing but sadness and frustration. You've taught me that the happiest place on earth can be and should be the home."

Everyone was touched and teary eyed, except Joey — who didn't fully understand the significance of what his brother had said. Mark had changed his whole outlook. Now he saw the world through the lens of the family instead of the lens of the "self."

"Mark, you remind me of a story from my life. I hope you don't mind if I share it," Sage began. "When I wasn't too much older than you, I married. Soon we were blessed with our first child. When my son was only two years old, I was drafted for battle in the European Theater during World War II."

"At first, things were okay. We traveled through the French and German countryside looking for people we could liberate. There were many camps, some to extract free labor for the Nazi war effort and some for extermination. We knew who we were supposed to be in the war. We were supposed to be the good guys; the guys who set people free. It was hard work, but fulfilling. There were times when our whole company marched through rough terrain all night just to hopefully arrive in time to save a few prisoners from death. You see, they would start killing the prisoners when they found out we were coming.

"One time we voted to miss sleep again and ran all night and arrived just in time to save about 150 people from death. They were still in line next to rows and rows of dead friends awaiting the bullet that would be for them.

"Another time I was with a small scouting group trying to gather intelligence about a concentration camp, and I was caught by a bunch of Nazis. I thought for sure they would kill me. I prayed day and night that I could return home alive to my wife and son. I told God that if he would help me get back home safely to my family, that I would promise to always serve him. Hopefully I've made good on that promise.

They put me in a Nazi prisoner-of-war camp. I was in an isolated cell in the basement of a cement building. I rarely saw anyone. For a year I sat in that cell or endured a torture session. You see, they thought that we had valuable information. They wanted us to divulge plans, and I think they also wanted to make us useless to anyone who might free us. They did awful things to me; I don't even like to think of it. They beat me, cut me, threatened me, starved me, and tried to get me to send bogus messages to the U.S. troops. At one point I was sure I would lose my mind from the isolation. That was probably the hardest part of the experience.

"I remember wondering who I really was, or if anyone even cared if I lived or died. Then came the day I had an experience that changed my life and my identity forever. When I went into the prison camp, I was a boy who thought his role was hero. When I left the prison camp, I knew my role was man, father, husband, and servant of God. I know it's funny to say, but now I'm actually grateful for that time in isolation.

"It shouldn't have to take the lowest times in our lives to put things into perspective, but sometimes that's how it happens. That was how it happened for me. One day, while sitting in confinement in my cell, I was looking at the gray cement wall and wondering if I would die there without anyone even knowing, or if my wife had already been told I was dead and had moved on to another person. Then I heard a sound. Out in the cement hallway, beyond the door, was the guard who gave us the meals through the slot in the door. On this day he started to whistle. I had never heard him do this before. He whistled a happy tune over and over again. Then it hit me. He, the enemy, could feel joy if he wanted to, even though he was surrounded by gray and dampness and awful odors, just like I was.

"This was a huge turning point for me. If he could feel joy daily being trapped in the Nazi army, guarding prisoners that to him were the bad guys and serving the enemy, which was me, then why couldn't I have joy too? This man on the other side of the door had something I didn't have. He had happiness. I wondered where that happiness came from while working in such a dismal place.

"Then it dawned on me that I wasn't happy because I wasn't even sure who I was anymore. And he was happy because he still had some of his identity. Happiness is a result of knowing our true identity. He knew who he was. He hadn't been sitting in the same place for months wondering if he was for real, like I had been doing. Depression, like I felt, led me to look at myself from a distance and ended up making me feel disconnected from myself most of the time.

"My brain started working. 'What gave a person identity?' I wondered. Surely I could figure out who I was and find some more strength to endure. So, I thought about my life. How did I even know I was a person? At that point I could have passed as a rock or a pile of straw. I was so lifeless.

"I reasoned, 'I had a mom and a dad.' If a person has a mom and a dad, well then they're a person! So, I was a son of two people. That was a start. As I pondered family more, I concluded that I was a father and a husband too. This was more regarding who I was supposed to be. I tried to visualize the faces of my family, but it was hard. I often felt like I was watching myself live. I had a hard time keeping in touch with reality.

"My mind wandered to other thoughts: 'Why was I here?' 'Why did I go to war?' 'What was so worth fighting for?' Of course, my family was worth fighting for. I went to war for my family and for other people's families. During my formative years, my parents taught me about standing up for what is right. They taught me about God and about His purposes for his children. My parents taught me that when someone was oppressed, God would have us sacrifice our own comforts to save them for Him.

"That was it. I was there for God. I was His child, and I was on His mission, and I was a member of a family. I had a role in my family now. That role had started a new cycle of life and created roles with my child. I was a father. It was this realization that changed me. I found my identity. It was my family that gave me my identity. God gave me to to a family, and the family — through its teachings — gave me back to God. I was to honor and serve both God and family. My role was formed from those two most powerful sources of truth in my life.

"There wasn't a need to fear death once I realized who I was. I didn't need to fear what would happen to me, what they took from me, or what they did to me. I only needed to fear God and remember Him and my family, and serve the principles my family stood for. I still had the family roles God gave me. I just hadn't remembered them for a while. I had been distracted by war. Mark, you reminded me of this story when you talked about the recent change you've felt from your family. That's what families do. They make us who we are. They give us our identities. All the other things in life are simply choices or experiences. The teachings from a strong family or lack of a strong family are the ideas, skills and principles that form us. You found a truth that will lead you to a life of purpose and happiness," Sage concluded.

"Now you know why roles are so important to us," Abigail said. "We weren't always perfect at roles, but we knew the principle. In fact, when our own parenting wasn't going so well, we remembered Olton's revelation from prison again and tried to build on it. We must always remember our roles. Who we are is always more important than what we do. In fact, who we are makes us fit to do the great things God intended each of us to do with our lives."

Jerry, with tears streaming down his cheeks, said, "Sage, I knew you were a World War II veteran, but I had no idea you went through all of that. The thing that sticks out to me about your story is the whistling. When you heard it, it seems you valued the man in the hall. You analyzed his role and saw him as a person with feelings and with hardships. You really saw him. When you took time to value him, then you were able to see his role more clearly. That one piece of truth you found about him led you to a great revelation for yourself. It sounds like if we forget who we are, we always get the opportunity to remember again because we're surrounded by people. Being grateful for them will lead to a better understanding of them and their roles, as well as our own."

Sage looked at Abigail, and she looked back him. After a second or two he spoke — deliberately, softly and powerfully. "Life is about roles. It's about what you understand about your roles, and other peoples' roles, as well as what you do differently because of your unique roles. Roles link us all together. They give us our identities. Identities don't create roles. Instead, roles create identities. Our society is struggling because we don't know who we are. Families fall apart if children and parents don't live their correct roles. A government becomes corrupt and falls apart if it don't know its role. A church loses its influence for good if society doesn't understand its role. And people don't find purpose or fulfillment if they don't know or live their self-evident roles. This doesn't mean all people or families have to look the same. It just means that each family needs to deliberately think about and take action on what roles they know God intends them to have with each other.

Sage concluded, "Every living and non-living thing has a role. It's part of the story of the world. To find more freedom we need to acknowledge true roles… and live them *deliberately*."

ABOUT THE AUTHOR

When it comes to parenting, Nicholeen Peck is a worldwide phenomenon and leader — and for good reason! Her proven system based on Four Simple Skills transforms even the most out-of-control teenagers and homes from chaos to calm within days. Though she's an international speaker, author, mentor, former foster parent of many difficult and troubled teens, and even President of the Worldwide Organization for Women (an approved consultant for the United Nations), Nicholeen spends most of her time at home with her husband and four children, which she knows will be her greatest impact and legacy. The fact that she has such an international influence while still being a stay-at-home mom is evidence of the effectiveness of her teachings. Learn more about her mission and methods at her website www.teachingselfgovernment.com.

124

Check out these and other resources to make your Family a success!

Parenting: A House United
ISBN 1492161578

Popular Parenting Methods
ISBN 1495949338

Find them all at
www.teachingselfgovernment.com/store

Printed in the USA
PSIA information can be obtained
vww.ICGtesting.com
TW052114271123
98LV00011B/697